Shawna Kenn... ...s, nanny, librari... ...duction assista... ...r, tour guide, re... ...r and dominat... ...s Angeles and serves as West Coast Editor of While You Were Sleeping magazine. She has written for Transworld Skateboarding, Metal Hammer, Slap, Heckler, Screw, Mix Mag, Epitaph Records, and Women in General, among others. *I Was a Teenage Dominatrix* won the 'Firecracker Alternative Book' award and was nominated for Independent Publishing's 'Most Likely to Be Banned' in the States. Film rights of this extraordinary memoir have been snapped up.

'Holder Caulfield in leather' Salon.com

'Shawna Kenney, in her memoir *I Was A Teenage Dominatrix*, makes her descent into badness seem sane and practical. Kenney's life in D.C. started off pretty typically: she liked punk rock and hated waitressing. But she soon began looking into new sources of income to pay her way through American University . . . After answering an ad in this very newspaper – "Get Paid For Being A Bitch" – she found out that she's a woman with a knack for making guys suffer. Good thing more young women don't read the classifieds.'
Washington City Paper

I Was A Teenage Dominatrix

Shawna Kenney

CORGI BOOKS

I WAS A TEENAGE DOMINATRIX
A CORGI BOOK : 0 552 15025 8

Originally published in the United States by Retro Systems
First publication in Great Britain

PRINTING HISTORY
Corgi edition published 2002

1 3 5 7 9 10 8 6 4 2

Set in 11/12½pt Candida by
Falcon Oast Graphic Art Ltd.

Corgi Books are published by Transworld Publishers,
61–63 Uxbridge Road, London W5 5SA,
a division of The Random House Group Ltd,
in Australia by Random House Australia (Pty) Ltd,
20 Alfred Street, Milsons Point, Sydney, NSW 2061, Australia,
in New Zealand by Random House New Zealand Ltd,
18 Poland Road, Glenfield, Auckland 10, New Zealand
and in South Africa by Random House (Pty) Ltd,
Endulini, 5a Jubilee Road, Parktown 2193, South Africa.

Printed and bound in Great Britain by
Cox & Wyman Ltd, Reading, Berkshire.

to Rich, the 'beautiful boy'

Much love and gratitude to:
Rich Dolinger, Harriette Wimms, Pleasant
Gehman, Carrie Dolce, Mark Pfau, Denise
Moore-White, Jennie Dunham, Tod Goldberg,
Cara Bruce, Clint Catalyst, Michelle Tea, Patty
Rocha, Iris Berry, Brandy, Missy, Beth, Pam
Gendall, Backwards-Hat-Tim Crean, Anja
Gustavsen, Rachel Resnick, Maggie Holliday &
family, the Dvorak crew, the Scherens, the whole
St. Mary's crew, 9:30 Club, Cesar (wherever you
are), Pete Koller, Lisa Holland, H20 boys & Moon
Morse, Ian MacKaye, Carlos Batts, Dito Montiel,
Adrienne Vrettos, Sander Hicks, Will Tupper,
Laura Barcella, Hilary Okun, Courtney Rubin,
Olsson's Books and Records, Atomic Books,
CityLights, Counterpoint crew, Martha Torrence,
Michelle Lauderbaugh, Leslie, Tony and Eric
Acosta, Yves Bauchet, Mark McNeely, Bryan
Christner, Susan N., Curtis Mead, Alley Emery,
Josh Hooten, Mike White, Nathan Kane, Elana
Roston, Shira Tarrant, Book Bound, Borders,
Stan Kent, Roger Gastman, Rose-n-Craig
Holloway, Matt Moneypenny at ICM, Steve
Lemons, Jason Tan, Dave Hooser, Lily Burana,
Jay Wiseman, Stabby, Tru Prey, Ann Cleary,
Mark Portier, Celeste Cleary, all former clients
and regulars, Diana Beaumont, Ron Turner, Last
Gasp, punk rock and anyone who has ever fed
or housed me. You have kept me and my faith in
humanity alive.
Everyone else can kiss my ass!

When I was around six years old, like most kids in my neighborhood, my sister and I spent summer days swimming at the YMCA. Some of the other kids got there earlier than us – they'd been swimming for hours already because they had swim lessons every morning. I asked my mom for lessons, but we couldn't afford them. I was jealous – not just because of their extra swim-time, but that they were already racing each other with awkward strokes back and forth across the pool, doing handstands and having underwater tea-parties, while my sister Ali and I were gripping the edges of the pool for dear life, still holding our noses like babies and taking turns going under.

I decided I would not be left out. When my mom was at the snack bar, I said goodbye to Ali and told her I was going to the forbidden zone – where I couldn't touch bottom. She protested with tears and four-year-old panic, threatening to tell mom, but the decision was

9

made. I had to push off that edge. I was going to make myself learn to swim. If I died, I died. I pushed off and my legs flailed in the blue depths beneath me. Kids all around splashed and screamed as usual, and I went down like the Titanic. Water rushed in everywhere it wasn't supposed to be. I turned my head in silent slow motion, from side to side, watching the colorful bathing suits and little legs around me. The lifeguard, still in her stand, was a distant red blob up above. I wondered when someone would see me drowning and come save me. No one did. My chest burned with chlorinated inhalations. Seconds seemed like hours until finally I flapped my arms and thrashed and wiggled my way to the surface. Sweet air filled my lungs and my nose burned like hell inside. I was near the middle of the pool, a good five feet from our precious edge. My sister was crying, waiting and watching in horror. I dog-paddled over to her and pulled up to the wall. `I can swim now,' I said smugly. She didn't speak to me the rest of the day. That's pretty much been my life. Sink or swim, trial-by-water. Whatever you want to call it. Sometimes you just have to get off that wall.

BEFORE

So, how did a nice girl like me get to be a dominatrix? Well, first of all, I'm a woman, not a girl. And what makes you think I'm so nice? Second, it's not as weird as you might think. I get plenty of questions and looks when people find out about my past employment experience. (Not exactly the kinda thing I put on my resumé, mind you.) True, I guess I don't fit society's caricatured idea of a 'dominant woman.' I'm a college-educated, petite, natural-looking woman with an 'Ivory Girl' sort of face. A pacifist. A former nanny, into music and literature. I don't dress in black leather, and I wasn't molested as a child or any of that crap. And I don't hate men. I like everyone, until they give me a reason not to. I'd love to tell you that I just woke up one day around age thirteen and said, 'I wanna be a dominatrix when I grow up!' But it didn't happen that way. I never knew that was a real option.

I always wanted to be rich and famous. Or rich and powerful, at least. Of course I had no idea how to reach these vague aspirations, but what kid does? So how did I come to spank men for a living? I suppose you want to know where I'm from – what my background is, what led me to this profession, and all that other Holden Caulfield kind of shit. All you really need to know is that I could be your neighbor. Your babysitter. Your student. Your waitress. Your friend. Your daughter. Maybe even your mother. We were all larvae in a cocoon before we became butterflies. Everyone's got a story. Here goes mine.

From goldfish and stray cats to lice epidemics and phonics, my childhood is alive and vivid in my head. Time-periods are mentally filed by television shows and places I've lived. The Sesame Street years were spent in Malone Village, a housing project in upstate New York, where I was born to twenty-one-year-old parents. My father received a telegram while aboard a naval aircraft carrier off the coast of Vietnam, announcing my birth. Eighteen months later, my little sister was born. My mom says there was never any jealousy between us, due to the fact that she prepped me for 'big sisterhood.' I liked help-ing with the care and feeding of the baby, and later took the role more seriously in preparing her for pre-school while I was in kindergarten. The Fat Albert years had us moving into a two-family home, which looked like a giant house from the outside but was split right down the middle inside. It was an orderly existence. The home was a tight ship run by my mom, with dad enforcing the discipline. Like most kids back then, we feared the belt, but didn't get it too often. If I was good, Sunday nights I could watch the Disney movie, savoring my one-Coke-per week snack allowance. If I was bad, bedtime was as soon as I acted up.

In school I was a quiet kid – so much so that teachers complained to my mother that I never raised my hand or spoke out loud at all. She was shocked because at home and in the neighborhood it was a whole different story. Even though I was small and younger than the kids who lived near us, I bossed them around quite easily. Bake sales, dance routines and games were all directed by me and run according to my rules, and if the gang didn't play right, then I refused to participate. Looking back, I realize how lucky I am that I never got my ass kicked, but for some reason, my tactic usually worked. At home, I was the same with Ali, but in a more benevolent way. Playing school, I had to be the teacher because I felt she had to know certain things before going on to each grade. I prepared lessons for her, showing her how to print numbers and pronounce vowels, just as my teachers did for me. So maybe I was a kid dominatrix and didn't know it. I don't know. Suffice it to say I had a great, if somewhat strict, childhood.

When I was twelve, we moved to a brown trailer in Maryland, on a plot of green land with a creek and a tire swing out back. We'd visited our uncles who were stationed there by the military years earlier. My parents had decided to get us out of the city, which was probably a good thing, though at the time we thought it was cruel and unusual punishment to be plucked out of school mid-year, sent away from our friends and cousins, and banished to a hick town. The only good thing in it for me was I had my own bedroom for the first time in my life. In reality, my parents were movin' on up like the Jeffersons because my dad got offered a better job, and my mom decided we were old enough for her to work full time, but being kids, we didn't appreciate this at the time. Everything about the move pissed me off. New kids who said 'y'all' and thought I was the one talking funny. New schools. No local YMCA. And no sidewalks for roller-skating, even!

It didn't help that it all happened around that lovely time known as puberty. My mom brought home a training bra because I was starting to develop, she said, and I wouldn't want people to think I was a tramp. Well I didn't want to wear one of those things, so as soon as she left the room I cut it up. I shredded the padding from the small cups with her big sewing scissors, snipped the dorky pink rose-bud from the center, and threw it all away.

When Ma returned and saw what I'd done she screamed at me, 'Do you know how much that cost me?! Fourteen dollars! Fourteen dollars of our hard-earned money! What the hell's the matter with you?' I saw the tears in her eyes and felt horrible. I didn't know WHAT the hell was the matter with me. But I still didn't want to wear one of those things. To me, that meant I was for sure a girl, and, I knew, all girls were wimps.

Later that year while watching *Fame*, my favorite TV show, my gender was confirmed. I'd been dancing around the living room pretending I was Coco and Ali was Bruno, then ran to the bathroom during commercials, wondering if I had somehow peed my pants. I saw the blood and knew. I checked again just to make sure I wasn't seeing things. It was all a mistake – I couldn't really be a girl! Bleeding every month would keep me from swimming or bike-riding or spending the night at friends' houses. And what would I say when my dad asked me to go fishing? I didn't want to be weak like Christy, the pasty vegetarian girl in my class who had stomach problems and couldn't participate in P.E. and wasn't allowed to eat anything good. I didn't need a 'monthly friend,' like my mom's. And I especially didn't want to have an accident like one of the girls at school did, having to call my parents and waiting in the office to go home with a sweater wrapped around my waist as everyone snickered behind my back. So I hid my under-wear in the back of a bottom dresser drawer, hoping I could escape my fate. I didn't tell anyone, not even Andrea, the girl in class who knew everything about sex and growing bodies because her mom was a nurse who gave her lots of illustrated pamphlets. I only played with boys at this time, I guess un-consciously assuming we were all the same. None of them could ever know, I decided. They might get grossed out or beat me up or just not want to build forts or play flashlight tag with me anymore. Eventually, though, my mom asked where all my underwear was going, and I had to 'fess up. She was mad that I'd kept it hidden, but after my tearful pleas she promised not to tell her gossipy best friend or my dad. As you can see, I definitely didn't celebrate my womanhood like Judy Blume's Margaret did. I basically just tolerated it.

I didn't really know we were poor until about a year later, when I was thirteen. Designer jeans and purses and shoes were in style, and I wasn't. In elementary school, everyone I had known lived in my neigh-borhood and lived like us. Our red brick apartment buildings all looked the same. But now we lived in a trailer, and in the private middle school my parents always reminded us they 'scrimped and saved' to send us to, every-one seemed to live in a real house and have things my sister and I didn't have. Their daddies hired magicians and rented theme parks for their birthdays, while my parents baked a cake from scratch and told us to be grateful for how 'rich we were in love.' I knew they were right, but the evil part of my heart wanted to be rich and famous, too. I longed to be popular and have the right clothes. I wanted cute boys to like me, and I wanted to be pretty. I wanted more.

When the purses with the button-on changeable covers were all the rage, my mom made one for me – sewn with her own two hands, and treasured by me, until someone made fun of it and I threw it down a sewer drain.

Being overweight made things worse. Eating pie one day at my friend's house outside under their new carport, my friend asked her mother for another piece. 'You'll be as big as her,' said her mom, nodding in my direction, making no attempt to lower her voice. My friend skipped the seconds while I finished in shame, then walked home adding skinny to my rich and famous goal. At least I was never the fattest or most picked-on kid or anything. Not like poor Pauline Parker, better know as Chicken Lips. Everyone said she smelled, and I never got close enough to tell for sure, but I studied her lips extensively while sitting across from her in Life Science one day, mentally concluding they looked perfectly normal to me – nothing chickeny about 'em. I felt sorry for her, but – grateful for my own invisibility – wasn't going to risk being friends with her, either.

By the time I got to high school, punk rock saved my life. Bands like The Dead Kennedys and Minor Threat made me think about politics and question authority. In D.C., a little over an hour away, the scene was a thriving cesspool of punk hippies making music with a conscience, and it rubbed off hard onto me and quite a few other kids. Every show we went to was some sort of benefit. People were active in trying to make their scenes and cities better, whether they were dishing out food for the homeless or raising money for local clinics. Or just singing lyrics that went against the status quo – lyrics that spoke to all my teenage rage and confusion with the world. Suddenly I didn't care about being accepted. My punk rock friends and I were the freaks of the school, but a least we were all freaks together. We ran the school newspaper, and I killed time skateboarding and cutting and pasting together a little photocopied outlet-for-my-frustrations called 'No Scene 'Zine,' while my sister was busy being a star field hockey player, yearbook editor, cheerleader and all-around popular student extraordinaire. I also played bass in a band that played a mean cover of 'Lola' but never made it past our living room. My friends and I all vowed to leave the county as soon as possible and never come back. It was normal for me to come to school with scabby knees from skateboarding accidents or wearing a brand new oversize T-shirt of some band I'd seen in D.C. or Baltimore the night before. So though I was the only girl in my group, I was definitely not girly. The guys I hung with were remarkable in that they treated me as a complete and total equal, and I am thankful to this day for the love and insight they shared with me. I learned a lot about men from this privileged insider's position, and little did we all know how handy this knowledge would be for me later on.

I'm sure nothing would have pleased my dad more than me enlisting in the military (like he had) or taking a nice, steady job on the government tit, but frankly, I was never any good at taking orders. I was arguing with the p.u.'s (parental units, as my friends called them then) constantly toward the end of my senior year. I wasn't a wild kid. I got average grades, played trumpet in the school band, and was even in the gifted and talented program, much to my embarrassment. It just seemed my parents hated my music, hair, and 'crazy liberal ideas' more and more each day, and I was getting sick of their if-you're-living-under-this-roof rules. I wanted to live under my own roof. It wasn't about drugs or alcohol, like with some of the kids I knew. I wanted real life experiences. Excitement. New faces.

New scenery. Something more than what I was seeing around me. I had no idea what I wanted to do with my life other than leave and live in a city. No one in my family had been to college, so though some of my friends were making plans in that direction, it never crossed my mind. All my parents asked of me was to graduate high school kid- and drug-free. Easy enough. I applied myself in school and graduated a couple of years early. Three days after graduation I moved two hours away to Washington, D.C., the closest big city I knew of, with my beat-up car, $400 in savings, and no fear of the unknown. Just a desire to swim.

FANTASY

No one told me that there wouldn't be many good-paying full time jobs for a seventeen-year-old with a smart mouth. I babysat for awhile, but was bored out of my skull talking babytalk all day and hanging with Oprah-worshipping nannies who didn't speak English.

I was a waitress for a month at a Holiday Inn, along with a forty-year-old named Renee who became an unwitting inspiration to me. Renee was a career waitress, 'a lifer,' (as she called herself) with no plans for anything else. Night after night, she desperately chased after the men who came in alone, each one a potential suitor who could take her away like Calgon. I quickly decided that a working class hero was nothing to be (sorry, John Lennon), and made plans to go to school someday. Until I could figure out how I was going to do that, I occupied myself by taking a creative writing class at a community college, booking punk rock bands part-time at a local club, and working in a daycare center, all at the same time. I was meeting all kinds of different people every day and I relished each experience.

I finally lost my virginity when I was eighteen. I'd been dating a pro skateboarder, and after a couple of months of teasing both him and myself decided I just wanted to get it over with and get out of club virgin. It was all terribly planned to the tee, right down to U2's *Joshua Tree* album playing in the background. He got out a condom and I looked away while he put it on, then it was over before I knew it. I broke up with him the next day, secretly deciding that if THAT was sex, I didn't need it and I was better off on my own, thank-you-very-much. Besides, I was kind of pissed that I never got a good look at his penis. That part of the male anatomy was still a mystery to me. I mean, I knew its general shape, of course, from all the jokes you hear as a kid, but didn't really know what it looked like, felt like, or could do. A few months later I met a brilliant, soft-spoken musician who became my willing subject. I decided I could date him and probably try sex again eventually. He was a handsome, older African-American man I met at the club I was booking. It wasn't long before racism reared its ugly head – not just in the form of stares or comments from other people, but from the people who had always told us to love everyone – our parents. His parents weren't too hot on the idea, but they quietly accepted me. Before I had a chance to get to know the guy, much less properly introduce him, my own parents got word of our budding relationship from the same old biddy who had called me fat when I was younger. She'd been up visiting D.C. and had seen us together at a local restaurant and apparently decided it was her Caucasian duty to inform my parents of my wicked ways. I was shocked at their reactions. I know now they just didn't know any better, but it caused me quite a bit of grief, and finally ended with them disowning me because I refused to break up with him.

I still find comfort in Henry Rollins' book *Hallucinations of Grandeur*: He nailed my feelings on being disowned, 'meaning the implied chains are off.'

Being cut off from my family hurt, but I'm not bringing it up to make them look bad. I just see now that whole turn of events freed me in a lot of ways. I've always felt I've had no choice but to follow my heart, approval and acceptance be damned.

My parents' rejection back then only pushed my new boyfriend and I closer together, of course, so we dated seriously for a while. It was us against the world and anyone who didn't like it could go fuck themselves. He treated me like a queen and we had some really good times together, although our relationship eventually ended for other

23

reasons. Responsibility and discipline have been my trusty survival tools to this day, and those are the gifts I credit my parents for. The rest – the bad stuff – I just chucked. You can only blame your parents for so much, I think.

I dated other guys – all different shades and colors and types. I dined with Ethiopians, danced with salsa instructors, flirted with DJs, wandered museums with tourists, picnicked with a Cherokee prince, and basically took every opportunity I could to get out and experience life with anyone who was interested. Then I decided it was time to get serious about my future, and clawed my way into college at the ripe old age of nineteen. Thank you, Renee.

All of a sudden my life was divided up into semesters. I had little money or understanding of the whole system. There was a point during first semester where I was actually homeless, living on friends' couches and in my car, even staying in a boys' dorm for two weeks (while a friend's roommate was out with mono.) So from the beginning, my college years were not typical. How could I live in a dorm with a bunch of 'kids' who were going crazy being out on their own for the first time? Most of them were only a year younger than me but I felt I was way too mature to live with them. They'd never lived in their cars. They didn't scrape by on ramen noodles. They didn't even pay their own tuition. They drove $40,000 cars and had pre-purchased meal-cards. I finally rented a small room in a big house with a bunch of weirdos of all ages. Unlike the wide-eyed eighteen-year-olds in my classes, no one was making me go to college, so I'm sure I was a real nerdwell to them. I loved school. No one was on my back about grades or boys – I was my own taskmaster. And my own worst critic. Each day I had a 'to-do' list and if I didn't finish it by bedtime, I'd stress and lie awake. I thrived on structure and discipline. Chalk it up to having a Navy father and going to parochial schools, but they seemed like the only things that made any sense. They got me through. I was the epitome of the 'birth, school, work and death' ethic – only it seemed like I lived it all every day.

It was cool having no one to answer to at the end of each day, but I had no one giving me any answers either. The school part I could handle, it was the cost-of-living part I couldn't figure out. School costs money, and freedom has its price. I bounced checks, ran up the shiny new credit cards I'd accumulated, piled up parking tickets, and learned how to eat for free by scarfing up food from receptions I had no business attending. As far as I was con-cerned, a date meant a free meal, too. The two hundred dollars a week I got for checking out videos to cranky students at the school library just wasn't enough to pay for the roof over my head, bills, food, books and all those other hidden collegiate expenses I was slowly discovering. I decided I had to create my own 'financial aid,' and one day, while flipping through the sleazy ads in the weekly city paper, I wondered if I could ever – gulp – be an *exotic dancer*. I'd heard of all the money those girls made and that sure sounded good to me. It's not like I thought I looked like all that, but I had guts and I was desperate.

I answered one of the more pleasant-sounding sleazy ads and made an appointment to meet Margarite, an agent who ran her own service. Margarite, a Mexican woman with bleached blonde hair and lots of make-up that didn't hide the deep brown road maps on her face, was an ex-stripper who was older than my mother. She invited me in to her cruddy apartment and started to ramble right away. 'Most of my men are lonely. They just want someone to talk to,' she said in a slightly accented nasal tone as she smoked a long skinny cigarette. 'Root beer?' she asked me, in between puffs. I nodded. 'They pay $150 for an hour with you. You get seventy dollars and any tips. You talk and dance for them.' I thought I could definitely gyrate and talk for that kind of dough, if she'd hire me, that is. I wondered how many other girls were up for the position. 'They love to see a pretty young girl like you. When can you start?' she asked. Flattered, I told her right away. So yeah, I was a teenage dancer first, but that's not all that interesting or unusual now, is it?

My first few calls were outcalls – which meant going to motel rooms and apartments to dance naked in front of a single pathetic guy while he masturbated. As soon as he was done, I could go. A typical night went something like this:

I knock on a hotel-room door. A man opens it. I'm smiling. He thinks I'm smiling at him, but really I'm just remembering the horrible Tina Turner imitation I do on the phone for my friend Tricia: a screaming version of 'Private Dancer.' That's me! Stripper. Exotic Dancer. Whatever you want to call it. I'd ask him for the fee, count it to make sure he wasn't ripping me off, walk it down to my car and lock it in the glove compartment (leaving my bag in the room, so they wouldn't think I was trying to pull something), and come back to dance. Margarite told me to say, 'Make yourself comfortable' to them instead of telling them to get naked, because if it was an undercover cop that could be interpreted as an invitation for sex – prostitution. Most of them pulled their pants down right away and just went at rubbing themselves. It was the ones who didn't that worried me. She'd told me if they didn't take anything off, it was more likely they were cops (or 'vice,' as she called them.) I guess if they were gonna do a sting, the officer wouldn't want to be caught with his pants down and his dick up. If they kept their

27

pants on, I tried to get a feel for whether they were just shy or if they were undercover by asking them questions and telling them, 'I won't watch if you don't want me to.' If they still stayed clothed, they definitely weren't going to just come if they weren't touching themselves, so it sucked for me because it meant I had to stay for the whole damn hour. Plus it just felt weird to dance nude while the other person was fully clothed. It was unfair, somehow. Luckily that only happened a couple of times.

Nudity never bothered me so I wasn't ashamed of that. And there was certain power in being across the room from a man and able to turn him on. At first I felt I was *pretending* to be sexy and they were suckers falling for it. It was pretty flattering that someone would actually pay to look at my body. I felt special, knowing I could make a man's dick hard. Of course, now I know that's really not too difficult a task, but at the same time I really thought I was 'getting away with something' somehow. Like, didn't they know it was just me – an overweight girl who's 'one of the boys?' That's how I saw myself at first, anyway. No, they never found me out – because I figured it out. All they know is what you tell them and show them. If you act sexy, they will buy it, and if you start to believe it yourself, that's what you'll become. I did wonder why they didn't just get a porno movie or magazine or something, but hey – if they had the money to blow, what did I care?

They'd always ask, 'What kind of music should I put on?'

'I like all kinds,' I'd say in a saccharine voice. Just like the song I couldn't care less, as long as they kept their grubby paws off me and hurried up with their release (as we so politely called it in the business.) I just tried to think about something else while I smiled and gritted my teeth and they ogled me. *When is that term paper due? I wonder what time the museum opens tomorrow? What bands are playing here this weekend?* 'Make him come so I can go,' was my secret mantra.

I hated when they talked. I tried to take control of each call, but one 'turn around and show me that ass' reminded me of my duty – to please the loser who had just handed me $150, and to do it without compromising myself too much.

'You have a nice ass. You ever had anything in there?' a guy might ask.

'No,' I'd say, facing the wall so I wouldn't have to look at his stupid on-the-verge-of-orgasm face.

'Would you like to?' he'd ask, getting all hot and hopeful.

Make him come so I can go.

'No, would you?' I'd shoot back, and then he'd get mad.

'What'd you have to say that for? Aw, Jesus.'

29

I couldn't help myself. My natural inclination was to take control of each call. Humiliate. Resist. Defend. It was a constant battle with my nature. I didn't want to please them or make them happy, and I deeply resented taking their money. I hated needing it.

I kept working at the school film library and did outcalls to motel rooms and middle class houses once or twice a week. I didn't tell anyone about what I was doing. I'd heard the things people said about strippers, that they were prostitutes or crackheads. I used to think those things myself. Even my politically correct punk rock friends would disapprove, I thought. I didn't feel like explaining myself to anyone, and my busy life kept most people distanced enough so I didn't have to.

REALITY

One night Margarite set me up with what she called 'a fantasy call' back at her place. She said the guy had a little girl fantasy, and since I looked younger than my nineteen years, I'd be perfect. When I arrived, she had a cute pink-and-white checked gingham mini-skirt made out of plastic-y vinyl-like material waiting for me. I'd never seen anything like it. She told me to go put it on, along with a newly bought plain white T-shirt, white bobbie-socks, and black patent leather Mary Janes. I even put my hair in pigtails to add to the part. I'll admit I looked pretty cute, and I hoped I'd be allowed to keep the adorable shoes.

'Now, don't fuck this up,' she said to me while we waited for the man to arrive. 'This man is paying me a LOT of money for this, that's how I could buy those clothes for you. He has a "little-girl" fantasy and that's what I want you to be – a cute little girl.' I said all right, not to worry. I looked like a damn little girl, all right?

The man arrived and he was heavy-set and gray. Well-dressed. Could've been one of my professors or something. He checked me out and whispered something to Margarite before retreating to the bedroom. I started to get a little nervous, wondering what I was supposed to do, but she pushed me into the room before I could ask. He was nude and sitting on a chair. His clothes were folded neatly in a pile just to the right of him. He patted his leg. 'C'mere and sit on my lap, honey. Aren't you just the cutest little thing?' he said. I asked him if he'd like to see me dance instead, and he shook his head no. 'Come sit with me and keep me company,' he said, again patting his leg. Since I was fully dressed, I reasoned it would be okay. I walked over timidly, and sat down sideways, staring away from him, at the door. He put his arm around me and breathed into my ear. 'You sexy little thing. You're a little tease, aren't you?' I looked down at his skinny legs and wondered how they could support his enormous apple-shaped body at all. I admit I was shocked. His lizard-skin hand moved up to my hair, down my shoulder and then onto my breast. He timidly fondled it through the T-shirt while I sat frozen. I'm sure I was shaking. I didn't know what was expected of me and felt too weak to say any-thing. I noticed he was shaking, too. I wondered why he has this fantasy and if he ever did this to any *real* little girls. Maybe he wouldn't, I surmised, if he came to people like me to get his jollies. Now I don't think so. Maybe he was a pedophile. Or maybe it was 'just a fantasy.' Who knows? He made me sick, though, so finally I got up and walked across the room.

'Would you like to see me dance now?' I asked. He was hard and started lightly stroking himself. His pubic hairs were gray.

'No, why don't you just sit down and show me your panties while you touch yourself?' he said. I agreed to the unusual request, at this point stunned and disgusted with what I'd done with this pervert and happy not to have to undress. I sat down and rubbed my under-wear and stared at the ceiling, not wanting to see the white stuff come out when Chester finished.

He eventually left. I don't know how much he paid Margarite, but I only made my regular $70 for the humiliation. I went home and threw the whole outfit in the trash. I beat myself up for letting things get that far, then promised myself I'd never tell anyone and it would never happen again. From then on, I danced at least six feet away from the men, staring them right in the eyes so I wouldn't see their penises.

Talking seemed pointless most of the time. I'd only do it if they paid me extra. I could never mention a price because if they were wired that'd be prostitution, Margarite said, so

I had to be tricky about it. 'Will you talk dirty to me, baby?' they'd beg, pitifully, stroking all the while.

'That's extra,' I'd say, smiling, running my hands along my thighs and hips.

'How much extra?' they'd ask, slightly annoyed.

'You get what you pay for,' I'd say.

Some would stop right there, but most would shell out at least a twenty to start with. 'Mmm, what's your favorite part of a woman's body?' I'd ask. I'd never seen a porno movie or even a sex magazine at this point. I just used every bad word I knew and things I heard my male friends talk about as material. When they answered, I'd say something stupid about that part of me, like, 'Mmmm – you like my tits? What would you like to do to these tits?' in a breathy Marilyn Monroe impersonation. I'd keep the eye contact and lick my lips and smile. 'Would you like to stick something in between these things?' They'd get all excited and ask me to talk dirty some more. 'That's all you get for twenty dollars,' I'd whisper. At that point some would be agitated by the obvious game and just hurry up and jerk it to get out of there. But to my amazement, most stopped stroking and fished into their wallets for another twenty to sixty dollars! These were tips, and they were all mine, according to Margarite's rules. Sometimes I was so good at getting them, I even amazed myself.

'Mmmm . . . you like my ass? Look at this pussy. You like my – oh, you're finished?'

'Have a nice night,' I'd say, throwing them a towel and putting my clothes back on as quickly as possible.

Some of the outcalls were scary, and I got the suspicion Margarite maybe led them to believe the hour was gonna include more than just dancing. She always denied it, but it pissed me off to get myself all made up, travel across the city, make introductions and then have the guy cancel when he realized I was only going to dance.

Some of them weren't so bad. Some were downright weird – like once I went on a 'social escort' call to play pool with a guy for two hours. He was a young, very attractive military doctor with no time for a social life. He said he was just sick of hanging out by himself and decided to pay a woman to play pool with him. He paid $300 for the two hours and tipped me an extra $100 because I was 'good company,' he said. I kept waiting for there to be a catch, but that was it. How did our world get to be a place, I wondered, where people pay for *friends*?

Another time I danced for a drunken asshole who actually fell asleep while playing with himself! I got dressed and left. He's lucky I didn't believe in stealing. I was glad to get off early anyway, in time to have dinner with my friend Tricia and some of her friends. I led her and everyone else to believe I was still waitressing sometimes, which I felt bad about. I hated dancing, but once I figured out how to take advantage of the men, the pay and the tips initially convinced me it wasn't such a bad job. Later, the hours I spent dancing and fending off advances filled me with stress and animosity I'd never known before. I felt I was on the defense constantly.

One night two drunk Marines grabbed my bag in a hotel room before I could even start taking off my clothes. They said they'd give it back if I gave them what they wanted. To their surprise as well as my own, I screamed like a maniac, snatched the bag back and ran out of the room, my chest threatening to burst wide open with every pounding heartbeat. I don't think I'd ever raised my voice in my whole life before this particular night. I didn't even know it could get that loud. To my embarrassment the hotel manager met me in the lobby and asked *me* to leave, like I was some cheap hooker causing a disturbance at the Super 8. 'I'm on my way out, motherfucker. Now leave me alone!' I yelled. Invigorated, I laughed all the way back to my car, forgetting how scared and cornered I was just a few minutes earlier. I guess I was learning to take care of myself, and if that meant some Marines were gonna be hurt by me, too bad.

Another time I went to dance for a couple in the city's most expensive hotel. I walked into a huge, plush Elizabethan-style suite to find a man in his sixties and a woman in her forties. The man was dressed in a suit and tie and the woman wore a green satin camisole and tap-pants. After explaining to them that my service did not include sex but only nude dancing, they said they understood and paid me $200. I ran the fee out to my car so it'd be safe, just like Margarite said, and returned to find the woman pouring me a soda. Then the man offered me coke. A little confused, I said, 'No, thanks, I already have a drink.' I looked over and saw him bent over the arm of the couch, snorting cocaine, and realized what a naïve idiot I was!

There was no tape player in the room and I didn't bring my box, so the woman put on MTV and asked me to begin. There were no videos playing – it was just some game show, which was kind of weird to dance to, but it looked like I didn't have any choice. They were on the couch staring at me, waiting for a show. When I took my top off she com-plimented me on my 'perky breasts' and asked if they were real. I assured her they were and she asked me if she could feel them. I said no. Then she told me hers weren't. 'Wanna feel them?' she asked, lifting up her top. 'I just had them done.'

'No, thanks,' I said. 'You know the service is only dancing, right?'

They looked at each other and smiled. The

man got up and walked toward me.

'We've done this before, in San Francisco. How much do you want?'

'I don't want any more money,' I said politely, 'I just don't have sex for money. I already told you that. Now I have to call my agency.' I lunged for the phone and called Margarite.

'Tell them they'll get their money back, go down to the car to get it, and then whatever you want to do from there is up to you, honey,' she said, and hung up. She was never any help.

I left the room but never returned with the money. I reasoned it was rightfully mine for the bullshit I had to put up with. Plus I needed it more than they did. I guess it was wrong to take it, but I was young and scared and mad.

The next night Margarite gave me one of her regulars – a Middle-Eastern guy in his forties. She prepped me by saying he had lots of money and was a big tipper if I played my cards right, he was her best client and I was lucky to get him and I was not to let her down. I waited for him on a lumpy chair across from the bed in Margarite's room. He had to duck in the doorway because he was so tall. He had a nice smile and wore a beautiful brown tailored suit. 'You have gorgeous eyes,' he told me as he entered the room. 'Thank you. Do you have the fee?' I asked. He looked shocked. 'Margarite doesn't make me pay until after,' he said, obviously a little insulted. It was highly unusual – she had told me before to always get the money first, that way if they decided to back out at the last minute, I could take out a $50 cancellation fee before giving them their money back. But since he was my employer's best regular, I agreed that would be fine to pay me afterward this time. I told him to get 'as comfortable as he wanted to be,' also as Margarite had instructed me to always do. He stripped totally naked and sat on the bed.

'Come over here with me,' he said.

Keeping to my six-foot rule, I stood up and said 'I'll be dancing from here.'

He stood up and walked over, his huge frame hovering above me, his chest near my forehead. He placed a heavy hand on my shoulder.

'Margarite said you were nice. Aren't you going to be nice to me?'

'I am being nice,' I said, slipping out from under his grip. 'There's no touching, you know.'

He laughed. He went to where his pants were on the bed, reached into a pocket, and pulled out a wad of money. He counted out seven hundred-dollar bills and folded them into my hand. I'd never held so much cash.

'And there will be a big tip for you after. I promise. Now will you be nice?'

I dropped the money and excused myself

from the room. Back in the living room, Margarite was talking to a caller, 'She's very young. Brown hair, blue eyes, 36-26-. . .' I signaled to her that I needed to talk. Clearly annoyed, she said 'hang on, please' to the caller and covered the mouthpiece with her hand. 'What's wrong?' she hissed.

I tried to explain to her what happened.

'Now is there touching allowed or what?' I demanded to know.

She got the caller's number and hung up.

'Letting him touch you for money would be prostitution. Tell him that.' She said it to me slowly, like I was a baby. Smug and armed with her answer, I turned and headed back to the bedroom. She was right behind me. She took my hand and placed a plastic bottle in it. I looked down and it read 'antibacterial lubricant.'

'But if you do decide to do a little something, honey, use this,' she whispered in my ear.

I walked back into the room in shock, wondering what the hell just happened.

'Ready?' he asked as I entered. He was lying spread-eagled on the bed. My stomach lurched and my brain searched for something to say. How was I going to get out of this? My mind said 'fuck it,' deciding there was no smooth way. No more Ms Nice Girl.

'I'm not going to fuck you, no matter how much money you have,' I said, as confidently as I could. My voice was scratchy and weak. I cleared my throat, and heard a voice booming – mine! – 'Maybe Margarite fucks you, but I won't.'

His eyelids lowered and he got up and pulled his pants on. I wanted to get the hell out of there, but I stood there paralyzed, watching him dress hurriedly. He leaned in close to my face and said 'Stuck-up American bitch!' then slammed the door. I rubbed the back of my hand up and over my cheeks, wiping away the bits of spit he'd sprayed on me with his insult. Then I collapsed into a ball on the floor and cried. I didn't know what I was doing or why I was in this woman's crappy apartment. I felt scared and alone and stupid. 'I am more than my body. I am more than my body,' I whispered to myself through the tears. Margarite entered a few minutes later, mad, of course. I realized I just wasn't nice enough for this line of work, and quit. Nice gets you nowhere. Went home and read Rollins, vowing to grow into the rage-driven monster he calls himself. I needed those words.

METAMORPHOSIS

Back to poor-paying dumb jobs. Whatever. I
waitressed again, faking a pleasant person-
ality nights at an Italian restaurant, and for
extra cash I wrote term papers for rich Arab
kids at school. Not something I felt great
about, but hey – I didn't have anyone helping
me. I knew I'd figure out something better. In
the meantime, I forgot my problems after-
hours by hanging out at local clubs where
I was known and got in free whenever I
wanted. I'd dropped my baby fat – no special
diet – just poverty and life on the move, and
the boys were noticing. Definitely weird for
me.

I became a regular at the Cro-bar. Filled
with bikers and tattoo artists and punk rock, it
was my own version of Cheers, starring me . . .
as the female Norm! Going there I pushed the
limits of what a short skirt was and how little I
could get away with wearing, and I really dug
watching the reactions. I came to be known by
the guys at the club as a dick-tease 'cause I'd

never go too far with any of them, and I truly cherished the title. I was picky and felt I had every right to be. I didn't really want to get involved with anyone. It seemed like it would just take up too much time and energy, plus I couldn't fuck the school thing up. Night after night I watched with fascination while women shot up in the open stalls of the black musty bathroom there. But I never did a drug myself. Never smoked a cigarette. Rarely even had a drink. I couldn't afford any vices, financially or mentally. I was the weird girl at the bar doing homework.

The staff and I entertained ourselves watching the strange 'romantic' alcohol-induced decisions people there made every night. I deflected any advances that came my way. The bands and company there were good. More real to me than the kids at school, whom I just didn't feel I had anything in common with.

The best guy-friends I'd had in high school were fading, moving away and getting into relationships. Not to say it wasn't a kick to see their tongues hanging out when they saw the 'new and improved me,' but we just weren't close like we used to be. I mainly had my new girlfriends: Sara, my neighborhood buddy, and Tricia, my beautiful every-hot-blooded-stereotype-you-could-think-of Nicaraguan girlfriend. She was my former boss-turned-friend from a retail job that didn't work out.

'You were the worst salesgirl I ever had,' she'd remind me, teasing, and I agreed. I simply was not good at being fake. I couldn't try to convince some poor sucker customer of something I didn't believe in. I told her that when I quit, and she accepted it and loved me anyway. Being that she worked full time and never complained about anything, she was the kind of girl my dad would've said, 'had a good head on her shoulders.' For Tricia and me a perfect night together was an evening of pizza and TV, gossiping and sharing dreams – real decadence, huh?

Sara was my neighborhood friend. We met my first day there in a little corner market. 'I didn't think white girls lived here,' she said to me at the counter while milling through boxes filled with tacky key-chains and gum. 'I didn't think black girls talked to white girls,' I said. We've been tight ever since. She was wilder than most of the other girls I'd known. We'd go out dancing and flirt with guys whenever I had the time. We even had an elaborate story made up for them, about how my mother married her father and now we're sisters – stuff like that. It always freaked them out. School and friends were my life. I guess you could say I was pretty much a normal girl before *the change*.

It's not like my hair turned black and I sprouted red nails overnight. I was just plain sucking as a waitress at the Italian joint. I didn't give a damn about the customer and wanted nothing more than for my shift to end quickly and painlessly. The best thing about the restaurant was that I could eat for free. The chef, who doubled as a bouncer when necessary, loved me and prepared anything I wanted. The worst thing was my boss who stared at my chest while he yelled at me.

The day before Halloween of my freshman year was horrible. My car broke down in the middle of a busy street on the way from school to work, so I talked a cab driver into pushing it to a local gas station for me, and left it while I scrambled to the restaurant for a double shift. I had no clue as to what to do about my car. I had no money saved, so whatever was wrong with it, I couldn't afford. That night an old bag who'd been nasty to me ordered a cup of decaf after her meal. We were extremely busy, my hair was falling in my face, I was sweaty and covered in food-stains, and I'd already screwed up some other orders. When I went in to the kitchen to pour her a drink, the decaf coffeepot was empty. For the sake of time and just plain meanness I poured her regular and brought it back with a smile. That's the way I handled most emergencies there. Anything to shut them up. I cleared a hundred bucks in tips that night and knew I could probably get my car fixed soon, which allowed me to collapse and enjoy the luxury of deep sleep.

The next morning thoughts of what Sara's sister did for a living ruled my mind and yanked me from my dreams. Sara told me that

Rochelle was a dominatrix, which meant she was mean to men all day long and got paid $150 an hour for it, and that it was a profession. Sara confessed she had even jumped in on a few of the 'sessions' herself for the extra cash, but that she wasn't doing it anymore because she was about to go away to law school and, 'Well, you just never know,' was all she said. Making that much money for what seemed like such minimal effort just blew my mind, though I didn't seriously consider it for myself. I suspected Paul, an old acquaintance turned part-time fling-of-the-moment, would never stand for it. He looked good but could be such a prude sometimes. That's probably why I never went all the way with him sexually. I'd just sleep naked in the same bed with him when he stayed over. He called it 'torment,' and I called it a test of his devotion. I hadn't decided what to wear for the Halloween party we were all going to that night, so I thought maybe I'd dress as a dominatrix. It sounded so sexy and mysterious. I called Sara for some ideas.

Later that afternoon, I held a real whip from Rochelle's stash. I fingered the braided handle, imagining the wispy ends smacking hard on someone's behind. Ouch.

'And don't you dare lose it,' Sara warned, flipping her long black hair with her long brown fingers. 'My sister'll have your head.'

Geesh. Didn't know my prop was so

precious. I knew she meant it, though. Rochelle was not a woman to be messed with. She was a self-described '300-pound black woman with an attitude.' Put it this way – when I invited her to my friend's pool party, she showed up in a black oversized T-shirt with the words 'TITS, HIPS AND LIPS' scrawled across it in white, a bikini underneath – and nothing else. The black, blonde and gold braids that hung down to her waist and the red acrylic nails from hell, along with her loud voice all made her the center of *attention anywhere*. According to Sara, dominatrixes all wear black, sexy clothing – just as I'd imagined – but I didn't have anything like that. I didn't even own anything leather, so we improvised: tight black unitard shorts with fishnets underneath, borrowed black heels, a weird netty thing as a jacket, and a super-duper push-up bra, complete with big hair AquaNet-ed to the max. My transformation was complete with a tiny tube of Ruby Red lipstick. From zero to sexpot in under sixty seconds.

'I feel like I'm in a Poison video,' I said to Sara as we left the house.

'You look like it, too,' she laughed, through her green Martian make-up. 'Just kidding. You look great. Work it, girl!'

'Sexy momma!' That was Paul, yelling from the car, beer already in hand. Fake blood dripping from the professionally-done gunshot wounds on his forehead. He leaned out to kiss me.

'The lipstick! The lipstick! Watch the lipstick,' I said and turned my cheek. 'And don't get blood on me.' He settled for an air-smooch and we piled in.

It's unbelievable – the amount of attention I received at the party. As we walked up the steps to the house some guy knelt down and asked permission to kiss my feet. 'You may,' I said, playing along, quietly hoping they didn't stink. Then to my surprise and Paul's irritation, he did! Everywhere I turned that night guys were asking me for a lash from my huge whip. They addressed me as 'Mistress.' They stuck their butts out toward me and asked for spankings. I laughingly obliged. Women complimented me on my thrown-together outfit, and men either stared or begged for beatings! I was a hit! For the first time in my life I was not a tomboy or somebody's buddy or worrying about my weight or bills or anything. I was drunk on power and sex appeal. I started thinking that maybe girls were not wimps. And maybe all men didn't like them that way. I started thinking maybe I could do this. It sure wasn't hard and I really enjoyed the unexpected attention. Paul sat in the corner all night playing chess and drinking – by himself.

'It was a joke – they were joking,' I explained to him in the car, driving home, after we dropped Sara off.

'No it wasn't – they really wanted you,' he growled.

'So maybe I should've charged them,' I laughed.

It was all he needed to explode into a tirade about how he'd 'never allow me' to do anything like that, and did I want to be a prostitute and blah blah blah. I suddenly saw him the way I initially had – before I'd given him a chance and dated him for the last two months – as a former Marine with a good bod and no sense of humor.

We went to bed mad. Well, HE went to bed, and I just stayed mad. I lay next to him, pinching him, kissing him – doing anything I could to get him to stay awake and talk, but he didn't budge. The more he snored the more I hated him. I got up and watched infomercials for awhile, then stormed back upstairs around 4 a.m. to throw him out. (To this day I blame my ungracious behavior on those Susan Powter infomercials – 'Stop the insanity!'). He woke, his big brown eyes bleary, hair sticking straight up. His pathetic state made it easier for me. He had no idea what was going on.

'Out of my house!' I ordered.

'Wha? Huh?'

'And take your stinky socks with you,' I added, throwing the balled-up things at him. I didn't mean for them to hit his head, I just had bad aim.

'You're psycho. What the hell's the matter with you?'

'Sleep is more important to you than ME, that's what! How can you just . . . sleep like that when we're fighting?'

'We're fighting?' he asked. 'Can't we talk about this in the morning?' I don't know what kept driving me, but it was relentless. All of a sudden all the little things about him that had been bothering me for the last few months looked enormous. He picked his toenails, he told racist jokes, he talked down to waiters, his father paid his credit card bills . . .

'No we can't. Now get out.'

That ended that. He fumbled down the stairs, then with the lock and out into the gray November morning. I wept for a few minutes, then watched cartoons until my roommates came down and ran me out with the smell of their bad weed. I went back upstairs, stole a Pop Tart from the makeshift kitchen, and called Sara's sister about a job.

LESSONS

I went over to Rochelle's run-down brick row-house on a Sunday morning. She arranged to have one of her regular clients come over to demonstrate a session for me. While we waited for him to show, I noticed she wasn't such a great housekeeper. Her mangy poodle Poopie snipped at my heels while I cleared magazines off her loveseat in search of a place to sit. I guess she saw the disapproval in my face because she commented, 'Cleaning is Sara's job. That's why she gets to stay for free,' and rolled her eyes. She was squeezed into a black corset top and a black spandex mini-skirt, with her brown stomach poking out in-between. While she laced up some black patent leather knee-high boots, she talked and talked about how stupid men are and how she had all different ones paying all her differ-ent bills and the one who was coming over now worked on Capitol Hill and paid her car note for her in exchange for his sessions. I thought she was exaggerating until I saw her in action myself. The man finally arrived, looking so normal. I don't know if I expected him to have horns or antennae or what, but he surprised me by looking so normal. He was well-dressed and middle-aged. The kind of guy I passed all the time in the city – too old for me to notice or be attracted to. She hugged him hello and told him not to speak to me and that I'd be observing his behavior, then led us back to the 'dungeon,' which was a teeny room just past her kitchen. It almost looked like a porch someone added on for pets. It was about seven feet long and three feet wide with a furnace smack-dab in the middle. It looked like anyone else's pantry area, except for the chains bolted to each corner of the doorway and neat strip of paddles, whips and handcuffs that lined the walls all the way around. They squeezed in and I sat in a chair in the doorway, watching and hiding my smiles behind my hand as the session unfolded.

'Get undressed,' Rochelle said to the man. He looked at me and she walked over and slapped him across the face.

'Don't stare at her. I said get undressed, as usual. Pronto!'

I'm sure my eyes were huge, shocked at the outright violence and his toleration of it. He scrambled out of his clothing and hung it on a chair. Rochelle walked over and opened the lapels of his suit.

'Ralph Lauren. Nice,' she said, smiling. The

man just stood there, naked and pasty-white. I looked at his skinny legs and paunch, trying to politely ignore the little hard on he had going on, but of course that was impossible. As I was examining his private parts from afar, a black leather thing came into the picture and smacked the head of his penis.

'Why are you standing? You know you need to be on your knees in front of me!' Rochelle screamed, tapping him a few more times with what looked like a horseback riding crop. He fell to his knees and immediately bent over on all fours. I couldn't help but giggle.

Chelle humiliated her 'slave' by telling him he was so pathetic that he amused me, when really I was so nervous I couldn't think of anything to say.

She insulted him. 'You are a wicked, wicked little man. You may not tell me the evil you do, but I can see it in your face!' she growled, inches from his nose. It looked like she was going to bite it off. He hung his head down, clearly shamed and maybe even scared. *I* would've been, had it been me on that floor! Then she walked around him, her enormous breasts brushing against his face. She teased him with her voluptuous figure and promised he 'would never be good enough to touch.' She made him roll over and do tricks like a dog, then yelled at him for performing poorly, and made him do it again and again until she was pleased. She even pushed him down, got on the floor, and put his neck in a pro-wrestling-type headlock between her thick thighs. When he started turning red, she looked up and saw that I was getting a little scared and then she laughed and squeezed harder! After almost an hour of this, she sat in a velvety throne-like chair and ordered him to 'play with it.' I considered this to be such a private act, but I couldn't help but watch. It wasn't gross, like with the guys I danced for. He seemed to be concentrating hard, intent on 'coming for her' the moment she ordered. She counted backwards and told him if he did not come exactly at the count of one, she would send him away and he'd never see her again. 'Ten, nine, eight . . .' He unabashedly stroked and stroked until his penis exploded, and he came in his hand, just as instructed! 'One!' she yelled at the crucial point. If I hadn't witnessed it, I never would have thought such a thing was possible. Then came her words of kindness, while he remained still, looking down at what he'd done. 'Very good. See you next week, darling.' She threw him a roll of paper towels and walked out. I followed.

I knew I could do this. Even though my car wasn't working yet, and it was the middle of the month, and I still couldn't make rent, things were looking up.

A few days later, the time came to do a session of my own. As I waited for the man to call from a corner pay phone before he was directed to her house, Rochelle told me, 'Oh yeah, I forgot to tell you that you're supposed to be a real British mistress. They're very in-demand these days.' *Fuck!* How was I going to pull THAT off? I panicked. I found confidence in the form of a generous shot of tequila. By the time the doorbell rang, I was picturing my life as a bad sitcom: 'Tune in next week as Janie (my wacky sitcom name) dons leather and pretends to be a dominatrix!'

I teetered down the stairs in my too-big borrowed black stilettos, thinking of how unglamorous it would be for me to fall and bust my ass while a slave waited on the other side of the door. I imagined my head sliced open, blood gushing from the side, and Chelle screaming for the paramedics. Then me trying to explain to everyone at the hospital why I was drunk at noon, wearing a patent-leather outfit and balancing on six-inch heels a size too big for me. I worried this was the start of alcoholism. This is how it happened for people I'd read about. They drink to get through something, and then they need more and more to get through life. I prayed he wouldn't ask me anything about England and opened the door. 'Entrez,' I said.

Shit, that was French, not British. Duh. He was a thin, well-dressed businessman in his forties. 'Hello,' he said back, nervously look-ing around the room.

I hoped he wouldn't run out due to the messiness.

'Your fee, please,' I said in the best fake British accent I could muster. He counted out $150 and handed it over.

'I want you in there, waiting for me naked and on your knees when I return,' I said, pointing him to the dungeon. Then I walked back up the stairs and dropped the money with Chelle. She took it with one hand while holding a Big Mac with the other, with her eyes on Jerry Springer the whole time. No 'good luck' or anything. When I returned, the man was naked as a jaybird, kneeling in front of the furnace and staring down at his already hard little penis.

'All right. Let's get started,' I said.

'Wh-what part of England are you from?' he asked.

Shit, here it goes, I thought.

'London,' I said, gently pushing his head down to the ground with one hand. I grabbed a paddle off the wall and smacked his ass.

'And I'll ask the questions around here, understand?' I said with a hard swing to his butt.

'Yes, Mistress.' I tried not to talk too much. *He sees right through me, I'm sure. He knows I'm a fake, he knows I'm a fake*, I thought over and over. He didn't. Or if he did, he pretended not to. I figured it was the same as with all guys you're first getting to know – half of it was just showing up and being female, period.

I told him to offer me his 'bum' in the air (heard that in a movie once), and proceeded to paddle and paddle until his ass turned blood-red. Soon I realized he didn't care about the bad accent but seemed to be ecstatic just by being in the room with me, and my new role became real. The hour flew by, and I grinned all the way home, thinking of how I'd made $80 in one hour ($70 went to 'the house') – it would've taken me eight hours of kissing ass to earn that waitressing. No more food-service for me – EVER! And I never drank again.

I quit the restaurant and did a few more sessions at Rochelle's for about a month. Then I realized what a lazy lifestyle she had. I was going to school and out dancing and seeing bands and dating in my off time, but she was holed up in her house all day, every day – waiting for the phones to ring so she could reel in her next client. I think most of her money went to ordering three meals a day delivered to her home. Take-out boxes and wrappers littered her kitchen, and one day when I was looking in her bedroom closet to borrow some heels, I was horrified to find a stack of dirty dishes piled up on the floor! Her house was filthy and her clients were cheap. I realized she only worked when her bills were due, and I wasn't working enough. I took my new on-the-job training and searched the adult employment section of the weekly *City Paper* for another gig.

MIRANDA

GET PAID FOR BEING A BITCH. The ad captured my imagination. Why not, I thought? I have a little experience now, and I'd been called THAT name quite a few times before. I called and answered a string of questions by a pushy-sounding broad, the first of which was, 'So . . . how long have you been escorting?'

'Uh, I haven't. I mean, is that what this is?' I asked suspiciously, thinking of horrible Margarite.

'Good, no,' answered the raspy voice. I told her I'd done a little domination before. She asked me my height and weight and physical description. I lied about my weight, but when I said blue eyes she said 'Oh good, they love blue eyes!' and told me to meet her the next day at the McDonald's downtown.

'How will I know it's you?' I asked.

'I'll be the one all in Gucci,' she answered and hung up. I didn't know what that meant but I thought I'd figure it out.

I wore my black wool skirt, black tights, and

a gray angora sweater I'd bought on sale at Benetton (my biggest splurge ever.) I mean, what do you wear to meet a dominatrix in McDonald's? 'Are you Miranda?' I asked a well-dressed dark-haired woman in line. She wasn't. I got an orange soda and took a seat at a booth and pretended to read while waiting for the mystery woman. Why was I doing this? What if I'm not pretty enough? What it they want me to be a prostitute? What if I'm too fat? Just as I was about to get up to leave this crazy little adventure of mine, a woman with long dark curly hair and big green eyes, dressed in a black Gucci T-shirt and matching bag, dripping in gold jewelry, asked me my name. She asked me my sign, and when I said Leo, she said 'Good. I'm a Sagittarius and we get along. We're both strong signs.' I told her I didn't believe in that stuff and she just rolled her eyes and smirked, 'Typical Leo!' The voice now had a face. And the face became my friend.

Miranda smoked right in front of the 'No Smoking' sign in McDonald's, but no one came out to yell at her. I told her my poor-college-student stories of waitressing and babysitting and how I'd dressed up as a dominatrix for Halloween and had a blast spanking everyone at the party. I also told her how an old boyfriend and I had a huge fight and broke up because I'd been jumping up and down on the bed in a silly mood yelling, 'I'm queen of the world! I'm queen of the world!' It pissed him off for some reason and I never could figure out why. She laughed and said I was a natural, assuring me the days of financial struggle would soon be over. She could've been a motivational speaker. She was confident and focused. She spoke in a whisper at times, 'in case of cops.' She told me about a bust she'd been through recently and how she was jailed overnight for pandering (I looked that word up as soon as I got home!) She was younger than I'd imagined. Her smoker's voice and tough talk made her sound like an old, worldly Madam, but actually she was only a few years older than me. A former hairdresser-turned-call-girl who found her way into fetishes and domination. Turns out she even knew Margarite. 'That old hag's still working?' she laughed, when I told her about my experience. Then she told me a story about when she was a stripper and had a client that just wanted her to spank him and punch him in the stomach once in awhile. 'And there I was, doing my first domination session in jeans and a bra!' she said. From the way she handled herself I was sure she'd been dominant all her life and just never had a name for it. She explained to me what domination could include – smothering, crushing, nipple torture, cock-and-ball torture, whipping, spanking, bondage, humiliation. The words swam in my head and she promised to teach me everything, winking at me with one heavily mascara-ed eye. She was beautiful. We clicked instantly.

When we walked to our cars, she laughed at my eight-year-old Datsun. Before I had the chance to be insulted, she explained 'That used to be MY car.' She said yes, for real, she used to drive a little piece-of-shit Datsun almost exactly like mine, then pointed to the shiny black new Mercedes parked behind me that she now owned. I was sold.

Miranda's apartment-turned-dungeon was classy. Outside it was just another cookie-cutter Northern Virginia high-rise with a pool and hot tub, easily accessed from the Beltway and downtown. Inside she had a huge pink leather couch in the living room, (which I learned cost $5,000 when she yelled at one of the girls for putting her feet on it one time). In the back there were two bedrooms for sessions. The third bedroom was off limits – that was hers. She had a closet full of clean towels and an extra bathroom for slaves to take showers after their sessions. (Some of them were just out for their lunch hours, she reminded us.) One of the rooms served as the main dungeon. A large wooden X hung dead-center against the far wall. We called it the cross. It was an excellent bondage tool – something to tie slaves to while whipping or teasing them. Off to the side sat a spanking bench, which looked like a gymnastic horse topped with burgundy leather padding. Giant iron candle holders held big drippy white candles in each corner of the room, and equipment hung from strips that looked like those key-hangers every suburban home seems to have. The second room's centerpiece was a black canopy bed. It was more for the dancers Miranda employed. (Most of us were doms, some were strippers, and some, to my amaze-ment, were both.) I guess the guys laid down and made themselves comfortable while the girls danced inches away from them. If the second room wasn't in use, we could bring paddles or whatever we needed in and use it for domination, too. Angels and cherubs decorated the walls of the rest of the apart-ment – Miranda said they were to protect her. Her maid offered us tea and snacks while we hung out.

She called us her girls. 'Juanita, bring the girls some food' or 'Girls, keep your voices down – I could hear you cackling all the way down the hall,' she'd say. 'MY girls are the best-looking in town,' she'd brag to prospective clients on the phone.

'Who's this? Who the fuck do you think you're foolin'?' she'd ask of suspicious callers. 'I know you're a cop because cops don't know shit about domination. Now get off my line!'

She also kept a blacklist of previous problem clients. Each name and phone number had a symbol drawn next to it that corresponded to her own key in the back. Callers were labeled as *psycho*, *violent*, *prankster*, *cop*, *no-show* or *cheap*. She'd been in business in D.C. for a little over five years, so she knew most of the weirdo callers' voices right away. It seemed a little paranoid to me but she cracked me up!

Sometimes she ran her business from the speakerphone while taking private Tae Kwon Do lessons at the same time. Kick. Kick. Punch. 'Hello, how can I help you?' she yelled, as sweetly as she possibly could.

When she determined a caller was serious about setting up a session, the interrogation began. 'Are you a novice or have you done this before? Corporal or sensual? Light or heavy? What's your fantasy? Cash or credit card?' Then she got the number they were calling from (being sure it matched the Caller ID), hung up, and called them back. This cut down on the no-shows.

Her ads were the most creative in the paper. INCALL/OUTCALL/OUTLAW was the title of one. Or ON YOUR KNEES AND CALL ME, PLEASE. She put a lot of time into making each one a poem or clever prose, and it paid off – her phones rang non-stop. Her clients were 'good clients,' she assured me. Some were well-known businessmen and lawmakers, and pretty much all were wealthy. She stressed to us that client confidentiality was extremely important, otherwise they'd never return. She told us to ask them before the session whether it was okay to leave marks because some were married or involved and didn't want to have evidence of their visits to us on their bodies. A man leaving the dungeon and a man entering were never allowed to see one another because you never knew if they'd know each other from the outside, she said, and we wouldn't want them to be embarrassed.

She charged almost twice as much to her clients as Rochelle did. $200 for an hour, $150 for half. $300 if the hour included golden showers, dildos, or 'anything special.' And she never discounted her rates, the way Rochelle did when business was slow. We all made weekly drops to give her the cut (50% if you used her facilities, 40% if it was an outcall.)

There were rules. Accept the money and call it a tribute (in case the customer was wired, she said). Always get the money out of the room, just like Margarite had said, and if it was an outcall, phone her at the office to check in as soon as you got to your destination. She'd ask, 'Is the money out of the room?' then 'Do you feel safe?' and 'Do you need a safety check?' That was where she'd call the number back exactly a half hour later and ask to speak to us, just to make sure everything was cool and he hadn't gone psycho or something. I'd only say yes to that if I got a bad vibe from the guy. After our yes and no answers (the guy was in the room, usually – and all ears, of course) we'd begin the session. If the guy suddenly chickened out and wanted to cancel, we were to return the money to him minus a $50 cancellation fee for our time. This was 100% ours to keep. If he hassled you about the fee, threaten to make a scene. Most men would not want that to happen – especially not at the fancy hotels they were staying at – so you should always walk away with something, she said. Remind them they're lucky to get anything back. You could order him to come at the end of the session, but you didn't have to. And as soon as he came, game over. It was his problem if he could only hold out for five or ten minutes, but on the other hand, Miranda always told us not to blatantly rush them, or they'd feel cheated and wouldn't return. Customer satisfaction was important even here! Oh yeah, and always wear a g-string under our outfits so we couldn't be accused of prostitution. And never do dildo training with new clients (it was the only illegal aspect of domination) – that was a privilege earned only after a few visits. No dating clients. Any tips or cancellation fees we made were all ours – we didn't have to split them with the house. And always answer immediately when paged. Otherwise, we'd be fired. We gave her our personal schedules weekly and told her when we were available. No dressing like 'sleazy hookers' to outcalls, and no boyfriends or husbands allowed in her apartment while we were working.

And if we were ever caught stealing a client she promised to make our lives a living hell. I believed her. She told me of how a former employee keyed her car, so Miranda went to the private gym where they both worked out and taunted her until the woman attacked her. Miranda pressed charges and sued for mental anguish – and won. (Her lawyer was also a client.)

She knew we all depended on the easy cash, and like me, she hated unappreciative, spoiled brats, so if you pissed her off just a little bit, she'd go through a process she called 'starving' – meaning she wouldn't give you any work for a few days just to make you appreciate her and the opportunity you'd been given. It always worked.

Miranda's real name was Lisa, but we weren't allowed to call her that. We all had at least two names – a dom name and a real one. She dubbed me Alexis, and I thought it sounded as good as any. Then there was Ginger, the Amazonian red-head who was really Nicole, and Julianne, an older Italian woman whose real name was Jeannie, and Lily, the tiny Japanese girl who sometimes went by Jade, but I think her real name was Karen. We could call each other by our real names, as long as there were no slaves lurking around. You'd never want them to know your real name, Miranda said, so we tried to stick to the fake ones. It was all very confusing at parties. Alisha was our resident submissive. Miranda gave her that name and always called her that, saying her real name, Magda, was 'ugly and too hard to pronounce.' She was about four-foot-eleven, 150 pounds. When a guy wanted to come in to spank a girl, we'd use her, while one of us watched, for safety reasons. She was Middle Eastern and newly separated from an abusive husband. She came to the States to live with some relatives and could barely speak English. She didn't seem to mind her role. When I asked her about it, her round face smiled and she said it paid better than her job at Wendy's. Sometimes a client would want a dom and a sub. He'd want to see the dom spank her or order her around. I found I couldn't do it. I felt so bad about her whole situation, and just her being a woman – I felt she was my peer, so I couldn't hit her. I avoided doing sessions with her for the most part. Miranda made fun of her and anything she said or did. If Alisha wasn't up to doing an appointment Miranda would yell, 'You wanna go back to Wendy's?' or 'Do you know how lucky you are, that I even let you work here?' at her until she'd go in and do it. When Alisha was shy in talking to us, Miranda would take a drag on her cigarette, squinch her eyes, blow out her smoke and sneer, 'Submissive!' as if it were the worst insult in the world. The other girls made fun of her, too. It was like chicken-lips all over again. I felt sorry for her and wondered if that meant I was submissive too.

Miranda was on good terms with a few free-lance doms in the city, too, so it they fit a fantasy or fetish better than one of us, she booked her clients with one of them for a cut of the profits.

Miranda wouldn't let me work right away – I had to watch and learn *her way*. I laughed as she insulted a fat old slob for an entire hour, and later watched in horror as she caned a young Georgetown med student until he bled (and he thanked her afterward!)

'Don't you ever do that,' she said to me afterward.

'What?'

'Make them bleed. Unless you've seen them before and decide that's what they really want and need. Drawing blood is dangerous,' she said.

I agreed and continued to be schooled by her sessions. I was in awe during cock-and-ball torture – she wrapped dicks in spiked leather 'collars' and tied testicles tightly with ropes and clothesline. I am still amazed at what the human body can take! I learned about safe words that are given to a slave to use in case the pain became too much for him. Miranda was a true dominatrix, professional to the tee. She even accepted credit cards! The dungeon's name appeared on the bill as a random set of letters 'that could mean anything,' she explained.

I guess she decided I'd seen enough and was ready for action when one night she pulled me into a session. I'd been sitting on the couch, reading a Cosmo, when she came out and grabbed my arm.

'C'mon. Time to work,' she said hurriedly.

'Huh?'

She pushed a ball of shiny red patent leather into my hands and told me to go put it on in her bedroom.

'My guy wants a golden shower and I don't have to go. Meet me in the bathroom in five.'

I pulled the outfit on, sweating nervously and hoping I wouldn't be smelly by the time I got to the bathroom. She had him in the tub (for easy clean-up). I climbed up. With my tiny feet perched on the cold edges of the porcelain tub, I felt like a true goddess rising above him. My five-foot-two-inch frame became that of a strong miniature Amazon standing over her lowly serf. My breasts stuck straight out from my chest with the proud posture. I reached down and unsnapped the crotch of my outfit. I noticed the man gaping in awe at the first sight of my fair maidenhead, so I reached down and slapped his face for his insolent behavior. He winced, and I ordered his eyes closed. Then I ordered the cretin to sit on his hands, since I couldn't trust him to control himself. I crouched over, closer to his head. My thigh muscles bulged and ached delightfully with the pose. I could feel my full bladder strain against my stomach. All my life I could always pee – anytime, anyplace, with someone watching or not, didn't make a difference to me. My small bladder paid off in this field. My eyes must've been huge as I watched the yellow stream travel from me onto his face. He actually opened his mouth! I couldn't believe what I was doing. I peed on him and giggled as it splashed in his eyes. Oops. I didn't think it would burn. He was actually shuddering with delight, saying 'Thank you, Mistress. Thank you.' I got down off the tub, wiped, and threw the toilet paper at him, leaving him there for Miranda. I didn't know what to say to him, I was so embarrassed and freaked out. When he left and I was back in my regular clothes, she gave me $75 for that five minutes.

After that, anytime another dom couldn't 'perform' in this area, I came to the rescue. Nothing could've been more natural to me. I pee all the time anyway – why not get paid for it? Water sports became my speciality.

I've always considered myself average-looking, a real plain Jane. But Miranda had plans for me. She had business sense I didn't have: she advertised me as 'Alexis – the girl next door,' and I was instantly a hit. This was much easier than being a 'real British mistress.' We never ran pictures. All her ads were well-written classifieds in the local papers and creative line ads under Entertainment in the yellow pages. She painted each customer a beautiful mental picture of us over the phone and added, 'looks guaranteed' if she thought we were pretty enough. She'd give us fake measurements, emphasizing or de-emphasizing what the guy wanted. 'Guys don't know what those numbers mean,' she told me once. 'It just sounds good to them if you start rattling them off.' Full-figured, flat-chested, older or younger. She had a girl for everything, and if she didn't, she played it off like she did. An older dom with a younger one became a 'mother-daughter team.' A black woman was suddenly Jamaican, if exotic was what they wanted, and Monica, a Russian-born multilingual professional masseuse, was our resident European from any fill-in-the-blank country they wanted a woman from. There was also a transvestite named Christy, who we never met, but was kept on-call for occasional special requests.

Miranda let me wear her outfits until I got my own. (We were the same size, except her boobs were bigger. Nothing a few safety pins couldn't fix.) She didn't allow anyone else this privilege, and I was honored. I took great care to return them clean and in good shape. I wore red rubber dresses, black latex bodysuits, purple patent-leather teddies – all kinds of crazy stuff I'd never seen before. My waist would be squeezed in tight, my breasts pushed out and up with special bras and corsets. I could hardly believe the figure silhouetted in the dungeon's candlelight was mine. When we discovered my muscular calves were too thick for the knee-high boots the clients seemed to love, Miranda went out and bought me a beautiful pair of black platform-style heels. 'You're the dominatrix, so you're in charge,' she'd tell me. 'If they ask for boots, tell 'em to shut the fuck up, and you'll wear whatever you want.' That made me feel better. 'Plus most of them like big legs,' she added. That made me feel worse, but oh well.

She always picked me up little gifts whenever she went on a shopping spree. 'Here, I just saw this jogging bra and thought you could use if for your workouts,' she'd say. Or 'Take this chocolate candy home, I bought too much.' Most of the time if was 'Stay and have dinner – Juanita'll whip something up.' No one had ever been so generous to me. Her phones rang constantly. She paged me to work even when I was off-call and I developed a small stable of regulars. The new job was fun and so easy! I couldn't believe that just a month before I was avoiding bill collectors' calls and now I was walking out the door nightly with at least $300 in my hand – and for what?! Spanking some man who felt he needed it? Why hadn't I learned this sooner? I was the star of these men's fantasies, and I was the dominatrix and I was in charge – not them. The ruler, the queen, the BOSS. My favorite role!

I did incalls at night after school. I'd do homework on the pink couch while the other girls yelled at Jerry Springer or whatever else happened to be on the tube.

Sometimes I did sessions with Miranda, which were really fun. The first time we did a double she pushed the guy over the spanking bench and tied his hands and feet to its legs, while I flicked him with various whips, paddles and riding crops. She told him he was a worthless piece of shit and that spanking was too good for him. She asked me to go get a bowl of ice-water. I brought it back, and she dripped it all over his ass, then paddled one white bun while I paddled the other. Twenty minutes later that man walked out with the reddest butt cheeks I've ever seen. Now I know what people mean when they talk about a 'chapped hide.' I bet he couldn't sit for days. 'Don't worry,' she said to me as we changed back into our regular clothes. 'He's corporal. He loved it.' She was right – he sent us a bouquet of roses as thanks the next day! I noticed her sessions were almost always corporal, to the point of being brutal, even, and wondered if she really hated men. She dated occasionally, always going for model-type pretty boys, but it seemed like her independence was what was most important to her. 'No one can take care of me as good as I can, I guess,' she'd say after each one bit the dust, and I completely understood.

Back at school I was an intense student who rushed off after every class and made little effort to meet anyone new I might have to divulge my job to. At home I studied with my pager close by, in case Miranda needed me.

PETS

Chandler was a pet project of mine that I'm proud of to this day. He came to me through the ad in the paper, and it started out like any other session.

'State your name, slave.'

'Chandler.'

'Chandler?'

'Yes.'

'Awfully prissy name, isn't it?' I hated prissy men. Still do.

'Bend over.'

I brought the paddle down onto his behind swiftly and firmly.

'Yes MISTRESS, you meant to say, correct?'

'Y-yes, Mistress,' he answered.

'I hate rich spoiled brats with prissy names, understand? Now, why have you come to see me today?' I always liked to know whether they were novices (like me!) or experienced. A little bit of background helped me determine what they would need.

'I haven't been with a woman in ten years,' he whispered.

'So you come to ME?'

'Yes, Mistress. I want to know why. I need help. I want to be in love.'

Shit, I thought. This one was more complicated. I couldn't just yell at him and get the session over with. He was coming to ME for help?! What did I know about why he couldn't get laid? I decided I just had to be honest. The interrogation began.

'What do you do for a living?'

'Accounting.'

'Where do you live?'

'With my mother.'

'How old are you?'

'Thirty-five.'

I crossed the room and sat. Leaning forward, I pointed my finger and told him everything he needed to do to get his life in gear, the way I've wanted to tell so many friends but for the sake of friendliness found a more 'tactful' way of doing it.

'You need to lose twenty pounds, quit smoking – you smell like a fucking ashtray – get your own apartment, and get a hobby. Oh, and stop slouching! You look like Quasimodo!'

That felt so good! And the best part was that he took my advice! He wanted to please me, so he really worked hard to change his life. He stopped smoking that day. Our sessions began with mini-bootcamp exercises. Sit ups, push ups, jumping rope. B.F. Skinner would've been proud. If you're thinking I fell in love with one of my clients, you're wrong. There was just something so pathetic and desperate about this one – yet sincere. He really wanted to change and really needed my guidance, and I wanted to help! I wondered if I could recruit more like him and run sort of a 'reform school for losers.' Sometimes all men need is a little push from a woman.

Chandler eventually got married. He sent me a beautiful thank you note on his wedding day and I cried tears of joy for his success, knowing I'd never see him again.

None of these men turned me on in a sexual way. But I enjoyed what I did to them. I've always delighted in teasing guys in my regular social life. Still do. Now I was getting paid for it. And not feeling so bad about it, either.

I was always a little scared of the whole out-call thing since the Marine incident from my dancing days. Most of these men were truly submissive, so Miranda assured me they would never try to hurt a woman. Still, I didn't trust anyone one hundred percent, so I hired my friend Tony to be my 'driver.' Since I drove, he was really more like a bodyguard who rode along on calls with me. Tony was a short, stocky, heavily tattooed martial arts expert, and, at twenty-three, a gangster with a police record a mile long. I'd known him for years, as his was one of the many dicks I teased. He'd been after me to go out with him but I knew what a player he was. 'Hey baby, your father must've been a thief because he stole the stars from the sky and put 'em in your eyes' was one of his typical greetings.

'Fuck off, Tony. Go get me dinner, will ya?' was what I'd usually say. His tough-guy friends would stare at me incredulously, wondering how I dared talk to 'Tattoo Tony' that way.

I once heard someone at the bar describe him as 'a bad-ass that even the bad-asses are afraid of.' I knew I could get away with anything with him, for the mere fact that he wanted me. His nickname for me was 'Angel Face.' I always called him on his stupid lines and cheesy flattery and he loved it. He'd screw some chick then call me late at night to tell me how he imagined it was me the whole time. He never gave up trying and I admired his tenacity. Besides, I always had a soft spot in my heart for thugs like him. They got their street creds through smarts and strength alone. No trust-fund, no family business to inherit. He was a hustler like me. He would've done the job for free, but I paid him $20 per call to be fair. I sensed he liked the danger. I might have given in and gone out with my little 'half-man, half-bulldog' at some point if only he weren't so damn arrogant. I could never let him get his way. I'm not saying I never messed around with him, but we never had sex. I knew he hoped for more and I used that hope for my needs. He felt macho and remained frustrated in a humorous, good-natured way, while I felt protected. It was a perfect arrangement.

HONESTY

Miranda threw awesome parties. Birthdays, anniversaries, divorce finalizations – any excuse for us to dress up in our dom-gear and invite special slaves. I felt so sexy with my major cleavage and men groveling at my feet. I was an actress playing the most exciting part of my life. At school I was considered smart, but here I was called 'beautiful' – a word I thought was reserved for other people. For movie stars or swimsuit models. Not me. I'd been called ugly, cute, fat, chunky, chubby, pretty and okay in my life, but never *beautiful*. Miranda and the slaves said it with such sincerity.

Some of the slaves would serve champagne and hors d'oeuvres; others would wait patiently in the tub all night, praying one of us would grant him a golden shower. Doms would do sessions in each of the rooms, and we'd all generally mingle and have a good time. It was NOTHING like the boring frat parties I'd attended. Women ruled, and I liked that – a lot. All of this positive energy made me walk with my head held high all day long at school. I probably didn't look much different than before, but I felt stronger and sexier than ever.

I spent a lot of time with Tony, of course, running from call to call on the nights I was working. He always cheered me on before the sessions, telling me to 'give 'em hell' and high-fiving me when I managed the big tips. We got to know each other better over late-night dinners and getting lost in every neighborhood in the nation's capital. After I was off for the night, he usually asked me to drop him off at a club or a girl's house. Sometimes he'd spend the night on my couch. I never really knew exactly where he lived, and neither did his other friends, and I could only reach him by pager. One night we worked until about four a.m. and I was completely beat. While driving through D.C.'s multicultural Adams Morgan district, Tony asked me to make a quick right, then to park.

'You can stay at my place tonight,' he said. 'You're too tired to drive home, I can tell.'

Surprised at the offer and relieved at the idea of rest, I sleepily agreed.

'Park it here,' he said, 'And follow me.'

I followed him down an alley and he grabbed the bottom rung of a fire-escape ladder on the side of a brown brick building. I stared at him suspiciously.

'I lost my keys,' he said, 'Just hop up and I'll follow.'

He gave me a boost and I climbed up and up until the third floor, when he whispered 'Stop!'

He budged in front of me and crawled in through an open window, then turned around and offered his hands to help me in. I couldn't believe what I was doing, but it was exciting in a way. Once inside the dark room he led me to a futon on the floor.

'Shh . . . be quiet. My dad's asleep in the next room,' he said while fluffing a pillow for me.

'You live with your dad?' I asked, stifling a laugh.

'Yeah, he's an ambassador. He travels a lot so I usually have the place to myself. Tonight he's here. Don't tell anyone where I live, okay?'

'Of course I won't.'

'Now get some sleep,' he said, then rolled over and passed out. I laid there awake for about an hour trying to see through the darkness. By the moonlight I could only make out a few martial arts trophies and some Rosary beads hanging on a doorknob. Enough to convince me that it was, in fact, his apartment and not some random stranger's. I fell asleep thinking about what a sketchy guy Tony was, and how little I really knew him. Yet I was honored that he let me in to his world, and glad that he was part of mine.

I woke up and left Tony a little note before

rushing off to class the next morning. I laughed in the car, realizing I was wearing the same rumpled clothes I'd slept in and that I just climbed down a damned fire-escape to exit a building. It felt like my high school days. I realized that I was a little lonely. Sara went away to law school in New York and we hadn't really talked since I quit working for her sister. I'd kept my new job a secret from my other friends – afraid they'd get the wrong idea and not like me anymore. I felt I had nothing in common with the other girls at Miranda's dungeon, either. One was a mother of three who brought all her earnings back to an abusive husband, which I never quite understood. One was a lifestyle dom, who lived with two slaves full time, something I just couldn't relate to. It just seemed like WAY too much trouble. And the rest of the girls were dancers. All we had in common was that we all wanted money. And that wasn't enough to base a friendship on for me. I decided it was time to come clean to my own friends.

I was afraid at first. I don't know why – I didn't feel I was doing anything wrong. Call it intuition – or former Catholic guilt. I had to be a bridesmaid in an upcoming wedding for an old high school friend, so I told her first.

'I have something to tell you, Rebecca,' I said.

'You can't be in the wedding!' she said, expectantly.

'No. No. I can be in the wedding. Don't worry about that. I just want to tell you what I've been doing as a part-time job, and why we haven't seen too much of each other lately.'

'Don't tell me you're selling drugs!'

'Are you crazy?' I snapped at her. 'Why the fuck would I be dealing drugs?'

'Ugh, such language. I don't know. You're just making me nervous. What? What is it?'

So many thoughts went through my head. *How do I explain? Will she even know what it is? Does it even really matter? Should I just go home now?*

'I'm a dominatrix,' I said quietly, in a matter-of-fact way.

'. . . That's like someone who spanks men, right?' she asked.

'Uh, yeah, sort of,' I said, but before I could get any other words out she started crying.

'I'll pray for you,' she said. 'I can't believe the horrible things you've had to do.'

And she didn't even know about my dancing – now *that* was horrible. And how about bridesmaid duty – that's pretty horrible, too. Besides, I didn't *have* to be a dominatrix. I chose to be one.

'It's not like that. It's really not bad, 'Bec,' I said.

'I'm sorry but you are a sinner and I cannot have you in my wedding. I don't understand why you've decided to throw your life away.'

I decided not to visit her again. I didn't

understand her reaction. From that point on I knew I was doing something society didn't accept. Oh well, nothing new for me. I just had to be more careful of who I shared with. A few weeks later, I called Tricia and asked her to meet with me.

'Is the big dipper working?' she asked, suspiciously, referring to the joke-name we gave the generous ice cream scooper at our usual meeting place. I told her I didn't know, but just to meet me – I was going to explain why we hadn't hung out too much lately.

'A domi-what?' she asked in her Rosie Perez-like sarcasm when I told her.

'A dominatrix. I spank men for money, basically,' I explained.

'You have sex with them?'

'No!'

'Jerk 'em off?'

'No way! I don't even touch them!'

'But do they jerk off in front of YOU?'

'Yes – but only if I let them. I'm in charge. They'll do whatever I say.'

'Hmmm . . .'

I could tell she wasn't buying it. She sipped her float for a minutes and eyed me suspiciously.

'And that's a *real* job?' I knew what she meant. Whenever my dad saw how much sports figures and entertainers made he'd say, 'Work? That's not work! Work is a guy who gets up at five every morning, waits in the

freezing cold for the bus with his bagged
lunch in his hand, rides for an hour, then busts
his ass for eight more. *That's* work!'

'Whaddya mean, a real job? Yes, there's a
demand. Yes, I get paid to supply. Simple
economics.'

She smirked. 'Very funny. But weird. And
they'll do anything you say?'

'Anything.'

'And what kind of man does this?'

'All kinds. Mostly rich, white old farts. You
know – the enemy! Watch this.'

I pulled out my new cell-phone, at which
she rolled her eyes, and dialed Chandler.

'Chandler, this is Mistress Alexis.'

Tricia's big brown eyes got bigger and she
put her hand to her mouth to keep from laughing at my fake name.

'Be a dear and run to the drugstore. Buy me
some tampons – you know the kind. Oh,
and something for my cramps. Patricia would
you like anything? No? Okay, bring them to
me immediately. I'm at Ben & Jerry's, on
14th & U. And don't you dilly-dally around.
For every moment you're not here, you'll
receive a slap for the cramps I have to
endure.'

I hung up. Tricia just about exploded with
laughter.

'No you didn't!'

'Yes, I did. And I do it all the time.'

Chandler showed up in all his huffing and

puffing splendor in exactly 25 minutes, babbling something about parking.

'Shut up, slave.'

He stopped immediately.

'Now give me the goods and leave.'

'What, Mistress? I thought I'd see you, we could talk—'

'You've seen me when you didn't expect to. That's your reward. Wait, come here for a second.' He stepped in closer. I gave him two Midols from the new bottle. 'Take these since you're so darned cranky.' He took them and swallowed them without water. I knew they wouldn't hurt him – maybe relieve a little water. 'Now go! Leave my sight or you'll be sorry,' I said, shooing him away and showing off in front of my new audience.

'Yes, Mistress,' he whispered, with his head hung down. I knew he'd be tormented until our next session. Ya had to keep them on their toes, I learned. Tricia finally believed me and accepted that I was not a prostitute. Most of all, she remained my friend. She called me more than ever, asking for every juicy detail of every session.

DUPLICITY

Unlike most of my classmates, I was not in college to party, nor was I searching for a hubby. (We always said the sorority girls were working on their 'M.R.S.' degrees.) Second semester of my freshman year flew by. The new job and money freed me. I had time to study without worrying about work schedules. I had money to pay the bills and take care of things, should anything go wrong. I kept records of my weekly earnings.

> *Monday - $330*
> *Tuesday - $130*
> *Wednesday - $50 (cancellation)*
> *Thursday (off – exam)*
> *Friday - $200*
> *Saturday - $396*
> *Sunday - $200*

That was a typical week. The perverts got horny on weekends. They were broke at tax time. And work was always slow around holidays – especially Valentine's Day, when they'd most likely be obligated to be with girlfriends or wives. Miranda knew the cycle well and explained it to me. Though I had more free time and was not exhausted from being on my feet all night, I stayed extremely disciplined. Paul had always joked that I did more before 10 a.m. than most Marines did all day. No one could've made me study harder than I did. Days I inhaled Spanish, World History, African-American Literature and Human Anatomy. I wanted to be Renaissance Woman so I tacked a karate class on to my schedule to keep in shape and focused. I collapsed each night afterward, my muscles aching, a book by my side and a new thought to ponder. On other nights I was learning things I was sure my classmates knew nothing about. (How much weight *could* a set of human balls hold? Is it possible to pinch a nipple entirely off? Professor? Professor? Can you answer me?)

My new profession colored the world around me. I stared hard at every male passerby – was he a submissive? A foot fetishist? A toilet boy? I wondered what couples did behind closed doors. A child tying up her stuffed animals with a jump-rope spelled 'future dominatrix' to me. I felt different from all of my classmates and friends. I wondered if they could see it in me. It seemed as if certain professors responded to my new-found power. The world was Silly Putty. Everything I thought I'd known was stretched out of perspective and replaced by my new 'inside' view. I was privy to a kaleidoscope of desires and differences that I made no judgment on – just enjoyed watching and observing.

I gave Tricia weekly updates on the different clients I was seeing and things I was doing.

'Eeeeeuuu!' she squealed into the phone one night after I explained to her what a golden shower was.

'OW! You hurt my ears,' I joked with her.

'Sorry . . . but I thought only poor people . . . eat and drink their own stuff,' she said.

'These people aren't poor, honey. They're paying me a lot of money to do this to them.'

In fact, I'm sure none of my clients were scraping together the $200 to see a dominatrix. They were all well off, and an extra $100 for a golden or just because I found some reason to demand it was nothing to them. They always had plenty of cash in their wallets. The ones who didn't were sometimes allowed to clean or build equipment or pay for sessions with whatever they had to bargain with. Miranda didn't like to use them for cleaning, though, 'cause they never really did a good job – they were too caught up in being in the room with beautiful women, and sometimes misbehaved on purpose just to get our attention. I went on to tell Tricia about the few brown shower clients we had, and then about

Julianne, the one and only dom who would do them. I thought she passed out when the line went silent.

'No,' she whispered, shocked at the thought of someone shitting on someone else's face – by request.

'Yes, and it costs extra. $400,' I said. I loved freaking her out. I was my naturally reserved, calm self when I heard stories at the dungeon or read the latest fetish book Miranda had laying around. Even when I was shocked, I remained pretty stoic – it was just my Yankee nature. Tricia had no such filter. She gave all my early thoughts on my new world expression. She gasped and laughed and screamed in delight accordingly with every story. And in exchange she told me about how she tied up her different boyfriends on a regular basis. She'd take one of the ever-present sheer scarves from around her neck and lash one hand to her bed post, reach in her nightstand drawer for another one and tie down the other hand, then ride the unsuspecting 'victim,' as she called him, to the point of orgasm. Pretty good for a girl who grew up in Central America, drenched in a machismo culture that expected women to be subservient. I knew she'd make a great dom and I tried to get her into the business, but she claimed to be too shy. I think it was enough for her to live vicariously through me.

At first, finding my motivation was hard. It's

difficult to be mean and humiliate someone who has done nothing wrong to you. In fact, he has been a perfect gentleman, and has paid you an enormous amount of money and compliments. Now nothing he says or does can be right. He can never fully please you – that's the game. To these men, you are an unobtainable goal. A woman of commanding presence, poise, confidence and class. You are perfect, simply because you are a woman. Superior, in fact, in their eyes. They will obey and cherish your every order.

I ran into Ron at Miranda's not long after I started working there. Impeccable silver hair, three-piece suit, loads of cash in his wallet. As soon as he stripped, I remembered him from Rochelle's dungeon. She and I had done a double together where she was humiliating this guy beyond belief. I thought it was to the point of cruelty when she poked at the strange quarter-sized brown spots that covered his entire back and torso. 'What is that shit? Fungus?' she cracked. He just stared down at his penis in the position she put him in and never answered.

'I remember you,' I said this time.

He looked at me with a worried look on his face, thinking I knew him from 'the outside,' I guess.

'Remember Mistress Mahogany?' I asked him. That was one of the corny names she used.

He nodded.

'I used to work with her. Remember when she made fun of your spots?'

He nodded again.

'What are they?'

He just stared at me.

'I asked what are they, retard?'

'They're not contagious, I promise,' he stammered. 'The doctor thinks they're from Agent Orange that was used in Vietnam.'

I commanded him to sit still and tell me about himself. He squirmed and fidgeted and stuttered in answering all of my questions. I'm sure he would rather have just been beaten and sent away. I honestly wanted to know more about him and what kind of a life he leads when he wasn't paying $300 an hour to be subjugated. Turns out he was a card-carrying NRA member and head of some tobacco lobbying group. Three kids and a wife.

'Do you cheat on your wife?' I asked.

'Well . . . no, but I . . .'

'What? What do you do? Spill it!'

'There's a certain intern I have,' he said.

'Yes?'

'Well, she teases me. She wears low-cut blouses and short short skirts, so I, um . . .'

'Go on,' I said, with a swat to his behind.

'I squeeze her breasts and put my hand up her skirt. I mean, she lets me! I promised her a job.'

'I see,' I said coolly, not letting on that I couldn't believe how surprised I was that he was actually spilling his guts to me.

His confession gave me plenty of motivation for the subsequent brilliant sessions we both enjoyed. He was a real mother-fucker, and I loved making him feel like shit for cheating on his wife and harassing the women in his office. I never let him play with himself or come during our times together. One time he was really worked up, so I ordered him out of the dungeon. I told him it was time to go home, but first, if he had to, he should masturbate in the car. Then I watched out the living room window as that animal actually sat in his car and did it. He disgusted me.

'They've all done something wrong,' Miranda advised when I first started and told her I wondered why these men wanted what they wanted. 'Somewhere, somehow, all of them have screwed someone over and know they deserve it.' I wasn't so sure before Ron, but he proved she was right. Even if the others would never confess their weakness the way he did, I used his honesty as justification for the rest. He made it easy.

You are the dominatrix so YOU are in charge. Miranda drilled those words into my head and heart. All summer long my confidence blossomed, and I churned out sessions of pain like they were burgers at McDonald's. Not only did I have my role down pat, but also I started to see the sessions as a release for me – like stage-diving and skateboarding had been. Dominating was a safe way for me to get aggression out. I'd enter the dungeon most afternoons after classes and angrily turn off the radio slow-jams the dancers left on. Fuck wanting to sex anybody up. I wanted to *beat* them up and get 'em outta there. I wanna beat you up. Pumped with adrenaline, I'd pop in my own mixed tape and go through the drill that I had memorized.

'On your knees. No man may stand upright in the presence of a Mistress and no man may look me in the eyes unless instructed.' *You have the right to remain silent . . . you have the right to an attorney . . .*

'You have no rights here. You'll address me as Mistress Alexis, speak only when spoken to, and relish the privilege of being here, understand?'

Nine Inch Nails was the first on my little 'soundtrack of demise.'

'Yes,' he'd inevitably say.

Thwack! I slapped his face like the star of a Mexican novella. The sound thrilled me.

'You've fucked up already.'

'Yes, Mistress Alexis,' the slave would always say.

'Better. Now I'll grant you a safe word should the session become too much for your wimpy ass to bear. The word is: red. My favorite color. But I suggest you use it sparingly, or it will be revoked. You are here to test your limits.'

'Yes, Mistress.'

Madonna's Erotica album was the perfect follow-up.

For the novices, I'd use words like 'play' and phrases like 'you're here to entertain me.' They seemed to respond to the you're-my-pet-and-we're-gonna-play-games approach. Those were my two standard intros. The outro was always, 'Clean yourself up.'

The more experienced clients were a tougher audience. It seemed like they'd seen and done everything already and just wanted something different. Rather than recite the same lines I'd used on the novices, I invented different punishments for them – copying sentences over and over until their fingers hurt, or standing with arms apart, palms up, holding dictionaries in each hand like I'd seen the nuns do to bad boys in elementary school. I found myself repeating phrases my mother had used on me, like 'this is for your own good' or 'I won't stand for it,' and to my surprise, the men ate it up!

I even made them hold painful stretches that I myself had been doing in karate class sometimes hours before. I remained a stone-faced, irritated, bratty bitch through it all, rarely cracking a smile. With both kinds of clients, I got to be my naturally bossy, demanding self (times ten!) and each and every one of them loved me for it! My face disguised the pain I could inflict, and Miranda attributed this and her grooming to my success.

Before I got into this line of work, I had dated and dumped a lot of guys who just didn't meet my standards in the attention department, and my friends always said I was too picky for my own good. Sometimes I believed them and felt bad for so quickly dismissing most men. Not anymore. As a dom I learned I had every right to be picky and demand more from men. If they couldn't live up to my expectations, it was their loss, not mine. I dated occasionally, but never let anyone close enough to get to know the real me. It seemed too much of a hassle. I was so spoiled by the combined attention I received from my clients that no one man could ever quite measure up. Plus I was still picky. There always seemed to be a few men around who were interested in me, but I was more focused on school. There was Arty, a wealthy Jewish guy who worked for a major league baseball team. True, we never went on an official date together – I dragged him along on a photography shoot of D.C.'s homeless problem that I was doing for a class – but still, the whole time I felt like he was reading me his resumé. He bragged about how much money he'd made in such a short time, and how many houses his parents owned – and I wasn't impressed. It didn't help that he kissed me like I was his grandmother – gently and timidly. No passion!

I went on two dates with a guy named Sam, a muscular body-builder from the Cro-bar. I knew the second time we hung out it wasn't going to work out – we went swimming and he not only wore Speedos to the pool, but actually brought his own personal grooming kit along, not to mention the fact that he looked in the mirror at himself more than at me. Then someone told me he had a live-in girlfriend of three years. Ugh – the nerve! There were other guys who never called again after I told them what I did for a living, so I mostly kept to myself and kept my nose in the books. Even some of my punk rock acquaintances at the Cro-bar didn't know. I guess I thought it'd ruin their image of me as the 'sweet girl' they thought I was and I wasn't sure if or where working in the sex industry fit in with that. They made jokes and called me Cobwebs (as in cobwebs between my legs) since they knew I wasn't sleeping with anybody, but I shrugged them off, amazing even myself with confidence that there'd be plenty of time for sex and relationships in the future.

Some of my clients' poorly-kept bodies shocked me. I'd never really seen anyone over the age of twenty-five naked. Poor hygiene has always disgusted me. ('Men SWEAT and

STINK,' Miranda would say to us, 'So don't forget to keep a window open and air out the place when you're done,' she warned.) She was right – they do. Eventually I found the more I tortured and teased these men, the more I degraded what I truly found revolting, and told them what I *really* thought of them, the more they adored me. It was a perfect arrangement. 'Go wash your ass and come back when you're clean,' I'd say, and they did. Or, 'Shave that silly beard next time you come see me.' And even 'I want you to be wearing pink ruffly panties for me next time.' I had fun with it.

I also paid off my two maxed-out credit cards and even took a few weeks to backpack through Europe – something I'd dreamt about for years. Imagine, a girl like me saying *grázie* and waiters saying *prego* back. A girl like me touching the feet of Michelangelo's David. A girl like *me* standing next to Hans Christian Anderson's Little Mermaid for a picture. A girl like *me* swimming topless in the Mediterranean! I'd always hated my muscular legs but I was grateful to them for the first time. They took me walking up 622 steps of a cupola in Florence, running for trains in Switzerland, climbing rocks in Greece, and walking across the continent everywhere I could get to in a month. I wanted to stay but had to go back and finish school.

Of course, Miranda starved me when I

returned (she was mad about her number one girl being gone so long), but she got over it and I kept working.

The crossdressers were different than most clients. They tended to be more sensitive. Most of the time they just needed to talk. My first encounter with one was also my first out-call. I had just gotten out of class and my pager went off. I called Miranda and got the specs: It was a double (he wanted two doms) and he was a novice. He's into cross-dressing and may want a golden shower at the end. I checked my watch, started drinking the bottled water that was always in my car, and hopped on the beltway heading for his home. Within minutes I pulled up to the little white house with black iron gate Miranda described. As I checked my make-up, Julianne's red sportscar pulled in behind me. I was thankful Miranda sent her – she was more experienced than anyone else we worked with and I knew she'd know how to handle this guy. I didn't bother to call Tony because I felt safe with the two of us (we had our dom-bags full of 'weapons,' after all!) Julianne met me at the car, a vision in black. Instead of her mid-length brown curls today she wore a gorgeous long straight black wig that fell to her tiny waist, emphasized by her naturally huge chest and the solid black catsuit she wore. She flashed her warm red smile.

'Ready for some fun?' she asked.

'Hell yeah!' I answered, trying not to sound nervous. 'Oh, and if he wants a shower, don't forget it's extra,' I reminded her, at Miranda's request. She said Juli loved her work but tended to be a little too generous with the clients sometimes. As Miranda always said, 'Business is business. Anything extra costs!'

Julianne agreed and took no offense at my relay of the boss's message. A handsome young man in his late twenties opened the door before we reached it.

'Are we in the right place?' I asked.

'Yes, Alexis?' he answered nervously.

'Yes, and this is my friend Julianne. You can afford to play with both of us today, can't you?'

'Yes,' he said by the time we reached the door,

'Good,' said Julianne. 'Now may we come in?'

'Oh yes, sorry. I'm a little nervous. This way.'

He led us through a series of hallways. I noticed the photos of him and a blonde woman throughout. I guess Julianne did, too.

'Your wife's not gonna be home today, is she?' she asked.

'N-no. she's out of town. I promise. Do you want something to drink or something?' he asked as we reached the bedroom.

'No thanks,' said Julianne. 'We'd rather get started. I need to collect the fee and then we'll talk.' I was glad she took over. She got the money and ran it out to the car while I called

Miranda to check in. I scanned the bland room. The bed was a huge queen with white fluffy quilts and pillows. 'What's your name again?' I asked him.

'Steven.' I nodded, and looked to Julianne, wondering where to begin.

'Ready to have some fun?' she asked him playfully. He answered with an enthusiastic yes. 'Okay, this is how it'll go,' Julianne said. 'We're gonna go change and we want you naked and on your knees by the time we return. Got it?'

'Yeah.'

'And you've got equipment of your own?' she asked.

'Yeah, some,' he said.

'Good. Set it out for us. We'll be out in five.' We headed to the bathroom. I changed into a black, shiny rubber dress I'd borrowed from Miranda. Julianne just fixed her make-up and stayed in her street clothes. We returned to the room to see several dresses and dildos on the bed and Steven kneeling patiently with his head down. I walked over to examine the stuff.

'Hmmm . . . lots of pretty dresses. Look at this, Julianne.' 'Oooh, lingerie!' she said, holding up a red satin bra. 'I think we've got ourselves a little Barbie doll here, Alex.' She walked over and rubbed the bra on his face. 'Mmmm . . . satin. Doesn't that feel good?'

'Yes, Mistress,' he gasped, obviously enjoying

the touch of the fabric. Then she grabbed some fishnet thigh-highs. 'Put these on, honey. I wanna see if you have better legs than me.' I giggled. Steven slowly put them on. I handed him a purple velvet babydoll-style dress. He put it on over his head. Julianne turned him around to face himself in the long dressing mirror. She took his hand and made him stroke the dress. 'Feels good, doesn't it?' she asked.

'Yes, Mistress. Oh yes.'

I thought he was gonna have an orgasm right there.

'Put these on,' she ordered, holding up a large pair of black high-heels. He awkwardly slid them on and turned to look at himself in the mirror again.

'Look at how short that dress is on you,' Julianne said, lifting up the back of it enough to see the curve of his butt cheeks. 'You're a little slut,' she said, decidedly. 'You wanna be our little slut today?' He nodded slightly and before he knew what was happening, she whipped out some lipstick. 'Pucker up, baby. I like my sluts with lips,' she said. He turned his head. She grabbed his face with her long fingers, smushing his cheeks and contorting his face into a pucker. 'Don't you fight me!' she said sternly. 'You NEED lipstick, and I'm gonna give you lipstick!' Not really knowing what else to do, I stroked his hair.

'Do as she says, darling. It works better that way,' I said.

He stopped resisting and she applied the red to his almost non-existent lips.

'There. Much better,' she said, happy with her work. 'Now look at yourself.' He turned and admired himself. Then he turned facing me, and stared straight at my breasts.

'I just wish I had those, Mistress,' he said. 'You're so lucky.'

'Well, yes I am,' I said, smiling because I hadn't always thought so.

'Maybe we can help you,' Julianne said, coming to my rescue. I looked at her and she nodded toward the bathroom. I went in and she showed up a few seconds later. She pulled some balloons out of her bag and filled them with water. Then we brought them out, and put them in a big bra on the man. She finished his make-up job and I arranged a long curly blonde wig on his scalp. When we were done, we brought him to the mirror, and Julianne renamed him 'Stephanie.' He looked like a strange woman with five o'clock shadow, but was ecstatic with the results. Julianne started to instruct him to play with himself while looking in the mirror (Miranda told me some of them like to do that), but he didn't want to do it. She didn't press the issue. He sat down and talked to us as I changed back into my normal clothes and got ready to leave. He told us he's loved women's clothing since he was young. The colors. Fabrics. Silks, fur, stockings. He assured us of his heterosexuality several times. He thanked us for our kindness and we split. He made me sad, because he just seemed so unhappy in his male body (as I'd be – who wants that appendage and all that hair?) If there was a god, why would he create beings in the wrong bodies? It causes them such frustration.

A few weeks later, my second outcall, co-incidentally, was another crossdresser. He was way out in the suburbs of Virginia, so Miranda charged him $300 for the hour. I arrived at a small townhouse and a short, well-dressed Latin man who looked strangely feminine opened the door. He invited me in in broken English. Now I could see he was wearing a light pink lip gloss and false eyelashes. I told him I'd be in the bathroom changing, and ordered him to strip and wait on his knees, just as Miranda taught me, and as I did with all of my clients. He just stared at me, standing in the middle of a plush, white square of carpet, surrounded by shelves of books and those enviable knick-knacks of the well-traveled.

'Didn't you hear me? I said strip and get on your knees!' I knew Tony was listening at the door for the first few minutes, just to be sure everything went okay. If this jerk tried any-thing funny, his door would be knocked down in two seconds flat.

'Pu-pu-please, Madam. I don't want to do that.'

'I don't care what you WANT. I am the

dominatrix and you'll do as I say!' I was on my period, and believe me, there's nothing scarier than a dominatrix with cramps. I must have sounded especially evil.

Tears formed in his eyes.

'What's wrong?' I softened my tone. I didn't think he was dangerous anymore. Hopefully Tony got the same feeling.

'I just want to talk and be with you.'

The man offered me a seat on the couch.

'May I take off my shirt?' he asked timidly.

'Go ahead.'

He unbuttoned his white shirt to reveal a white corset that looked like it had seen better days – and even then, it was probably still ugly. He stared at me, as if to ask, 'is this okay?' I nodded. He unbuttoned his pants. He had on the biggest grandma-looking under-wear I'd ever seen. He looked down, ashamed.

'Does this o-o-offend you, Mistress?'

'No, why would it?'

He walks over to me and asks permission to lie on the couch, his head face up in my lap. I grant it, and we talk this way for the next two hours. I decide to test my third-year Spanish skills and he is thrilled with my clumsy efforts. *Diga me en Español*,' I tell him. He says he's a surgeon, originally from Argentina. His wife knows about his love for women's clothing, but doesn't wish to see it. He speaks too quickly and I tell him to slow it down, laughing to myself as I wonder why we've never learned vocabulary like 'crossdresser,' 'submissive,' or 'you need to get some better underwear' in class. Whatever would Professora Maria Helena think of how I'm implementing her lessons? I stroke his hair and tell him of the other men I've met like him, and he can't believe it.

'You mean, there are others?' The fifty-year-old becomes a child, his brown eyes big with joy and wonder.

'Of course.' I told him about the special closet at Miranda's dungeon, filled with furs, silky dresses, nighties, shoes and wigs for our crossdressers. He was in complete shock.

'I come from a country where it is very important to be macho. To be like me is a disgrace.'

'You are not a disgrace. You are just you.' I tell him. It sounds weak when I say it, but it seems to satisfy him. My friends always tell me I should be a therapist. That, or a bartender. How sad, I thought, to not be able to be yourself with your lover. I wonder if his visit with me made him feel better or worse. Better for finding someone who understands, or worse and frustrated for doing this behind his wife's back, suppressing his urges around her. Maybe it's no worse than some of my friends not knowing 'the real me' and what I've done in the past. People can be judgmental, so we have to keep our secrets. We said pleasant good-byes and he told me he'd call the agency when he needed to talk again. The day was a lesson to me – every session was different because each person was different. 'You are the dominatrix and you can do whatever you want.' Miranda's words echoed in my head. True, but I could not continue to go through the motions of spanking and giving orders in the same way to every client. I had to pay attention, and tailor each session to fit the person I was with. I had to get creative. Just like with school and life in general – I wanted to push myself to do the best I could.

About twenty-five percent of all calls were outcalls. They opened up worlds I'd never seen up close. I was going to the finest hotels in Washington. Marble staircases. Glass elevators. If I'd had a particularly hectic day and no time to eat a decent meal, I'd have the guys order room service in time for our session. Shrimp, cheesecake, salad. It was the first time I could look at expensive menus and order exactly what I wanted with no thought of price. In true white trash fashion, I even ordered extra appetizers and desserts – food I knew I couldn't finish – and took it home with me for the next day. The client never seemed to care. Half the time it was on his company's credit card anyway. I also got to explore some of the nicest homes. Houses you'd see in magazines. I had never been so close to such extreme wealth. Many rich older people lived alone in huge mansions, with their pets as their only company. They just indulged their fantasies once in awhile by paying someone like me. It was always riskier going to someone's house. I mean, who knew what they had planned? But I had Tony as backup, plus I liked meeting them in their own surroundings. Studying their books. Pianos. Closets. Medicine cabinets. (Oh, the medicine cabinets! I never realized what a medicated society we lived in until I started this form of snooping!' 'Anal-itch creme,' 'Anti-fungal ointment,' 'Flush-free Niacin.' *What is that stuff?*) Anyway, I think most were just plain lonely. Maybe even bored with life. I showed up at one guy's house on a beautiful summer afternoon. I don't know if he even knew what a dominatrix was or what, but he seemed extremely happy to see me. He introduced himself as Norman, welcomed me in and asked me to please have a seat on the couch. He fixed me a glass of ice water at my request, then sat down and put his face in his hands.

'You don't have to get undressed or anything. I don't know why I called you people,' he said.

'I wouldn't be getting undressed anyway, smart guy,' I tried to explain to him. 'I'm here to . . .'

All of a sudden he was crying. Big tears

rolling down from his eyes over his thin, aging hands.

'My wife died twelve years ago,' he sobbed. 'And I haven't been this close to a woman since.'

His chest heaved, he was crying so hard by this time. I was completely stunned. I hadn't prepared for this.

He went on, 'I don't know why I called. I just wanted to talk to somebody – a woman.'

I thought maybe he was getting some bright idea that I was some sort of prostitute, so I clarified that he was not going to have sex with me or any such thing. He sobbed harder. It wasn't what he wanted anyway. He really just wanted to talk. When I finally believed him, I put my hand on his back and smoothed over it back and forth, like my mom used to for me. His frail body shivered under the thin checkered shirt's cloth. He composed himself and stopped sobbing eventually, and then told me he was from Seattle but his daughter was attending school in D.C. When his wife died, his life ended. He was completely lost without her. He retired a year ago and moved to D.C. to be closer to his daughter. He was battling depression and wanted to try just about anything to get his life moving again. He told me he tried dating twice, but both times he felt so guilty about it. His wife was the love of his life and he didn't want anyone else. I had no psychiatric background, and being so young I had no experience with what he was going through, but I knew he had passion for this woman he shared his life with, and I was touched. I know I probably should've told him she'd want him to get on with his life and all those other things you're supposed to say, but to this day I know when I die I want someone to have loved me like that. I didn't know what to tell him, so I asked him questions about her, her likes and dislikes. I noticed a few antique cameras on display in a glass cabinet, and told him I was studying photography. He was so happy to take the cameras out and show me how they still worked. He pulled out photos of his wife and daughter, and I was sincere when I commented on how beautiful they both were. Our time ran over and my pager beeped. It was Miranda, calling to ask me if I was staying for another hour or what? If so, I'd have to charge him. I told him I had to go and he happily paid the $100 for an extra half hour with me (she marked the price down like that if we were already mid-session.) I couldn't believe this man was paying just for my company. Thoreau was right. The mass of men do lead lives of quiet desperation.

He called the agency a few more times to see me, always ready with stories and sometimes lunch. We never did anything sexual or acted out fetishes or fantasies, and Miranda never knew he was any different from the 'other freaks,' as she called them. I ended up giving him my phone number and stopping by – for free – to check in on him from time to time. From every job I've ever had, no matter how miserable or insignificant, I've walked away with at least one true friend. Norman was it for this one.

All of the outcalls were adventures into the unknown, and having Tony along made it fun and sometimes even more unpredictable. Once I finished a session early and came down to find him just digging in to a steak and lobster dinner in the hotel's bar.

'You can't be done yet,' he said, looking shocked.

'I am. He was a "minuteman." Now what the hell are you doing?' I asked.

'Having dinner – on Uncle Bob,' he said, winking at me and smiling at the bartender.

I suddenly realized what he'd done. Since he had all of my client's information, he'd gone ahead and ordered himself a nice meal and charged it to the room.

'Get it to go,' was all I said, rolling my eyes at his obnoxious move. 'And don't ever do this again.'

He proved to be very useful. I just had to learn how to handle him. I was on a call in cobblestoned Old-town Alexandria one night, up in a guy's walk-up loft, while Tony waited in the car, as usual. The guy was a sweet, timid nerdy sort (my favorite) and his apartment had a cozy cabin feel to it. He had a few candles lit, along with a blazing fireplace, both warming the room with an orange glow. It was picture-perfect, down to the German Shepherd sleeping in front of the flames. I ran the fee out to Tony, then called Miranda to check in and told her I felt comfortable, didn't need a safety check, and that it was only an hour-long call. The guy made me hot cocoa and we sat in front of the fire having an intense discussion about literature. We never even discussed the session. I guess I lost track of time and he was just getting up to grab a book off the shelves to show me, when there was a pounding at the door.

'Open up! Open up! You in there?'

Tony's voice boomed through. I checked my watch and realized I was a half hour over. I guess Miranda lost track, too, because no one had called. 'I'm fine, Tony. I'll be out in a little bit!' I yelled, then turned back and smiled sheepishly at my client. He pounded again and said he wasn't leaving until he could see I wasn't being held against my will. The dog ran down the stairs to the closed door ahead of me, barking his head off. The guy grabbed him and I squeezed by them on the stairs, whispering 'I'll handle this.' He pulled the dog back up to the top and watched as I opened the door. Tony jumped in with a gun aimed right at me. Then he saw me and pointed it at the guy. 'You have a GUN?' I shrieked. The

113

dog wouldn't stop barking and the guy turned about two shades whiter.

'What's up? Are you okay?' Tony asked.

'I'm fine, put that thing away,' I whispered angrily. I looked up at the man at the top of the stairs and said, 'I'm sorry. I'll be right back,' then walked Tony back to the car. He was raging because he'd been scared to death wondering what was going on up there, whether I was lying there dead or being raped or something. Miranda had paged him and said she'd been trying to call the man's house at the end of the hour, but there was no answer. Apparently he'd accidentally turned the ringer off. I had lost track of time completely, so I was to blame, too. It was a big, dumb mix-up and we agreed we needed a system, and I needed to stay aware of the time and remember that people were worried about me. Tony promised not to draw that thing again unless it was an absolute emergency. I didn't ask him how he got it or when. I didn't want to know. Finally, I went back inside and the man apologized about his ringer, then just gave me $100 extra to leave. Poor thing was scared to death by the whole scenario. By the time I got back to the car, Tony was shaking, too, I hugged him and gave him the hundred bucks as his tip.

Another outcall to a hotel was kind of sketchy. It was quite a drive away and Miranda asked who wanted to risk it. It was for $500, so, greedy me – I volunteered. She double-checked the name the man checked in under, got directions from the hotel, and I left with Tony at my side. I even called halfway there and spoke to the client, assuring him I was on my way. When we arrived, an hour later, the night clerk said there was no one registered under that name. I went to knock on the door number he'd given anyway, while Tony waited off to one side.

'I'll be right there,' yelled a deep voice.

'What do you mean? Answer this door right now.'

I didn't want it to be a cancellation. I banged on the door a few more times and no one answered.

Confused, I called Miranda from a pay phone. I guess Tony decided to stay behind and wait at the door. I was on the phone explaining what had happened when Tony came back with a horrified look on his face. 'Let's get out of here – NOW,' he said, grabbing my arm. Apparently the door finally opened and out walked a Lou Ferigno-looking dude, six foot six, according to Tony, with biceps as big as legs. I knew it had to be bad for my Tony to be that scared.

Tony said he asked him, 'Did you order a dominatrix?' like I was a damn café au lait!

The giant yelled 'No! Now get outta here.'

We bolted and assumed the desk guy must've been in on it as some sick joke. The guy got his jollies in cancelling appointments. I never took that risk again.

Another night we followed Miranda's directions to an industrial part of town. She said the client told her it would be hard to find the building, so she gave us his number to call once we were in the area. Tony and I switched places so he could drive and I could call and navigate. We turned into a warehouse-lined dead end, where there were no lights on and the building numbers were hard to read. I pulled out my cell phone and called the client's number.

'Hi, this is Alexis. I'm a little lost,' I said.

'You're in a white car. You're very pretty, but there's a man with you,' he said.

'Yes, that's my driver. Hey – where are you?'

'You weren't supposed to have a man with you.'

I hung up and ordered Tony to get us out of there – fast! He peeled out and we were gone in seconds. I still get goosebumps now, thinking about what that guy's plans may have been for me. Creepy.

Two weeks later one of Miranda's dancers got punched in the ribs by a client. She called the police and they already knew the perp. They laughed and joked with him, 'You at it again, John?' The police wouldn't let her press charges and the girl was so humiliated she just wanted to leave. I was so sickened by this I got a couple of Tony's boys to go over and rough the guy up the next night. I don't believe in doing such things nowadays – I've found that karma has a way of taking care of everything, but I was twenty and enthusiastically played the vigilante role just that once.

REWARDS

By fall of my sophomore year, business was thriving. Most of the other girls had moved on or been replaced. I made myself one of Miranda's most requested girls. I was always on time to appointments, ready with gear-in-hand, and best of all, in her opinion, I was sober. Plus she liked the fact that I never allowed any physical contact. I never touched any of them. Never allowed them to kiss my ass or be smothered by my breasts for body worship like I'd seen other doms do. Never even spanked them bare-handed. I wore surgical gloves for every session. I just couldn't stand the thought of a stranger, some-one I didn't love, touching me, but Miranda approved because she knew we couldn't get her busted for prostitution. Not all of the other girls drew such lines, and I think some of them resented me for it. I walked into a session during a party once to see another dom sitting on top of some handsome young man's face. He serviced her with his tongue while she tapped his penis with a riding crop. I was a little shocked, but to each her own, I say.

Miranda and I spent a lot of time together, doing sessions and just hanging out. She opened up to me and told me about her own poor, strict upbringing, and how her big family had no idea what she did for a living. She wanted to make a bunch of money and get out in a few years, and I wondered how she'd ever be able to do it, spending money the way she did. Still, I couldn't fault her too much for that, because I was always tempted to do the same thing.

I paid a price for being 'headmistress' favorite', though, in that I was paged at all hours of the night, and sometimes even during classes, when I was not supposed to be on call. It was an honorable yet annoying position to be in. Miranda had no idea of what life outside of her scene was, and I had lots of other things I wanted to do with my time. In the middle of Psych the last thing I wanted to think about was some horny slave's desires. School dead-lines paraded in my mind as I removed my sweaty patent-leather outfit at the end of my sessions. I'd shove the heels and clothes into my 'dom bag' (black – not to be confused with my green book bag, for school) and leave the dungeon as a Tasmanian Devilish ball of energy, heading for the computer lab or study group. It seemed my classmates were always partying, hanging out, and pondering what they knew of the universe in their spare time, while I had little time to spare whatsoever. The money from my job was great but I loved school and wanted to do well. I hadn't chosen a major yet, but dedicated myself to earning that degree. I would NOT be someone's secretary or laborer when I finished. But I also knew I would not be a dom the rest of my life, either.

Miranda rewarded me by letting me do the V.I.P.s (a.k.a. big-spenders.) Now I worked three nights a week, and made an average of $4,000 monthly. I hit the jackpot with a couple of loaded regulars who flew in to see me occasionally. The money thing was still a shock and I'll admit I went a little crazy with it. Miranda could relate – she came from nothing, like me. She was more than happy to do the girlfriend-let's-go-shopping thing with me. You can imagine what a young woman like myself making almost a thousand dollars a week does right away – she blows it. All I really owned to that point was a bunch of hand-me-downs and a milk-crate full of records that had survived the chaos my life had been before, moving from project to project with my parents, then to squatting in an abandoned building until I roomed with another girl in a trailer, then 'moved on up' to my furnished room (with shared toaster oven, sink and bathroom down the hall.) Eventually I moved into a nice brownstone on Capitol

Hill, where I could have my own things. Now I just needed *things*.

I denied myself nothing. I had my first manicure. Nice, but impractical, I decided. I chipped the white French polish on my car's steering wheel as I drove away from the beauty shop. Next came the clothes. I splurged on a $200 pair of heels, rationalizing that they were work-related. I also bought $100 worth of used clothing, which Miranda scoffed at. 'Why do you still act like you're poor?' she yelled. I just thought there was no sense in wasting money unnecessarily. And I'd rather spend it on music and books. I also bought my friends some ridiculously expensive dinners. Tried out every kitchen appliance imaginable (returning half of them – who has time for a juicer?) Then came The Car. He was someone I met on my own, and Miranda would've fired me if she'd known, I was keeping my own client on the side. I kept him anyway because I found him fair and square, just by talking to him and figuring out his deal one night at a dance club. It was my good fortune, and I didn't want to share. I'd seen him a few times for $300, guiltily keeping it all to myself. He was about to move away and get married so I knew we wouldn't be seeing each other for much longer. He paged me late one night as I was dozing off. Annoyed, I told him to call back in the morning. He wouldn't take no for an answer (uppity subs!) so I said, 'You'd better make it worth MY while' and slammed down the phone, leaving to meet him. I called Tony and we were off. The man paid $1,000 cash, and I gave him the session of his life. In mid-spanking with the hairbrush he loved so much, I played on his humiliation fantasy. 'Stay right where you are. Face down, ass up,' I yelled at him. He did. I poked my head out his front door and saw Tony reading a magazine. 'Psst! Fred!' I whispered. For some reason Tony wanted a 'code name' lately, too, so I called him Fred in front of clients. I guess he forgot because he didn't look up from his mag. 'FRED! Get IN here!' I hissed again. 'Just come in here. I want to show you something.' He shrugged and followed me in. The man's white butt was still in the air, showing splotches of pink from strokes of the hairbrush. 'Look at that ass, Fred,' I said in mock anger. 'Isn't it the most disgusting ass you've ever seen?' 'Uh, uh, it's pretty disgusting,' he stammered, staring. 'Give me your belt,' I said to him. He looked dumbfounded and handed it over. 'You see what you did?' I yelled toward the slave. 'You've disgusted my driver! For that I'll have to punish you!' I folded the belt in half and walloped him. The slave yelped but didn't use his safe-word, so I knew it was okay. I looked back at Tony and he was peering through the fingers over his eyes, watching but looking scared to watch at the same time. He'd never really seen me in action, and I think he was shocked.

Thwack! I smacked the guy again. 'I said your ass is disgusting my driver.'

'Thank you, Mistress,' he answered. His ass was still in the air and he was swaying, probably tired with the uncomfortable position.

'What do you think of that, *Fred*?' I asked Tony, smiling. Tony's mouth hung open. I turned back to the slave. 'Are you getting WEAK?!' I whacked him a good one across both cheeks and he collapsed onto his side, panting hard and begging for mercy. I looked back at Tony, and he backed away toward the door. He raised his thick eyebrows in sympathy, like he was scared I'd really injured the guy. I could see the pity on his face. My back was to the slave, and I rolled my eyes and shook my head at Tony – smiling, telling him everything was fine, not to feel sorry for the guy because he was getting exactly what he wanted. I shooed him out and closed the door before he ruined it with his sympathy. He waited in disbelief while I finished up inside. I ultimately left the guy tied up with the belt, and frustrated. I bought a new used car the next day – nothing as fancy as Miranda's, but the newest car I'd ever owned. At least it had power steering. Tony gave me a brand-new top-of-the-line stereo for it, too. God only knows where he got it. I didn't ask. I was too busy being ecstatic.

PUPILS

The clients varied in their tastes as much as their looks. An elderly man came in who wanted me to whip him as hard as I could. With every lash he moaned, 'harder, Mistress, harder!' I got sick of this Santa Claus telling ME what to do (plus my arm was killing me) so I kicked him out after about ten minutes, joking 'Guess I'm not getting any toys this year.'

Another time a client told me he was an accountant, but I just didn't believe him for some reason. I was getting good at reading these people (dom-intuition?). Finally he confessed his true profession.

'No need to forgive me, Father, for I know exactly what I do,' I quipped as I paddled the priest, 'and I like it.' I punished him for the 'impure thoughts' I knew he was having of me – and for the 'spilling of his seed' I knew he'd do later. He thanked me profusely and I snickered all the way to the bank. Vatican money hard at work. I was learning what a diverse city I lived in.

Once I had a school superintendent whose humiliation involved wearing a pair of Mickey Mouse ears.

I had a physician who wanted to lick the toilet clean. When I lead him into the bathroom to do it, I started to gag and ordered him to go home because his fantasy was making me sick.

An art professor became a regular of mine and asked if he could do a figure-painting of me. His wife knew about his S&M habit and had no problem with me sitting nude in their parlor while she and their kid and the two dogs ran around the house for a few Saturdays in a row. The portrait was just of the back of my body, sitting and twisted to the side, my face glancing slightly over my shoulder. It was breathtaking. (And he paid me full session price for every hour I sat).

I also saw a Nobel Prize winner for a light spanking session. (I didn't believe him when he first told me of his achievement, until I did a little research at my school library, and sure enough, it was him.)

Jonathon was a one-time client I'll never forget. When he walked in I was a little surprised. He was a good-looking guy in his early twenties. He dressed cool, listened to punk rock – he's probably the only client I ever saw that I actually considered to be a peer. It made me kind of nervous for some reason. He told me that he was a novice and had always wanted to see what S&M was about. He asked that I not hurt him 'too much.' I agreed and took his money. I started the session like most of my others, telling him to get naked and on his knees. He followed my instructions and I couldn't help but notice his lean, fit body. I put a dog collar on him and started in with leading him around the room like a dog. I noticed he was smiling a bit.

'Is there something funny, Mister?' I asked as I swatted his behind lightly with a cat-o-nine-tails whip.

He just kept smiling.

'Speak up. Is there something funny, I asked?'

He unhooked the collar from his neck and stood up, then burst into full-blown laughter.

'I just can't believe I'm doing this,' he said through his laughs. 'I'm sorry. I'm so sorry, Mistress Alexis. It's nothing against you. It's just not what I thought it would be. I don't know. It's too weird.'

I understood exactly where he was coming from, and burst into laughter myself.

'It is, isn't it?' I said.

'I don't know what I thought it would be. I just wanted to … experiment, I guess.'

'I understand. It's weird for me sometimes, too. It's like we're in a play or something.'

I took a seat on the floor, and he got dressed while we both talked about sessions and what they involve and why it's wild that people

126

experience these things with strangers. I offered him his money back minus the usual cancellation fee but he refused to take it.

'I wasted your time and I'm really sorry. You earned that money,' he said on his way out. 'Thanks for being so understanding.'

My time with him was anything but a waste. It taught me to have more of a sense of humor about my new 'career.' It was a funny, weird profession. And I'd been trying so hard to be the perfect dominatrix that I'd forgotten how to laugh and just be human sometimes – to be myself.

Sometimes I did Miranda's regulars if she didn't have time. Rick was one of those. He was a famous voice-over actor and I recognized it as soon as he spoke. He had a menstrual fetish. He paid me to save my used tampons wrapped in foil in the dungeon's freezer for him. Once a month he'd come and make his 'pick-up.' I was afraid to ask what he could possibly want with the things, but finally got up the nerve, and he told me he used them as stirrers for his morning tea. Pretty gross, I thought, but I made $300 a month off of something I would've just been throwing away anyway.

I also had a roadie for a big rock band as my own regular. He was a 300-lb. Harley-riding tattooed and bearded hunk of man who just loved legs and feet – the sweetest, most respectful guy you could imagine. He'd rub lotion onto my feet and we'd talk music the entire hour. He indulged me with rides on his 'hog' and got my friends and me backstage passes every time he and the band were in town.

I had another guy who owned a vending machine business, so I made him bring me rolls of quarters (in addition to his tribute) so I'd always have laundry money.

I loved to get lobbyists and lawyers. They seemed to know they were everyday assholes, and I tormented them for all the sexual harassment scenarios and male-chauvinistic behavior I imagined them to be a part of. My anger with them was sincere. They were the type of jerks my mom had to fetch coffee and type her fingers to the bone for – the kind I despised the most. Their snobby attitudes, their mid-life-crisis sportscars, their decaying bodies, their bad comb-over hair-dos. I couldn't imagine anyone falling in love with them or wanting them sexually. I truly hated every inch of this type of man, and it paid off. They loved me for it.

The wildest night was the bachelor party. When Miranda first asked me to do it, I looked at her like 'I KNOW you're not asking me to STRIP for a goddamned bachelor party.' I got over it when she explained it would be me and Julianne, doing a dom-scene for a group of about ten guys. I was nervous. Even though I performed these scenes every night, it was just for an audience of one, not ten. But I talked to Julianne and felt better. She said she'd lead the way, and it would all be fine. I knew she was very experienced and had done stuff like this before, so I trusted her to follow through. Miranda gave us the specs way ahead of time. I spoke on the phone with the groom's best man, the host of the event, and he assured me the groom was really into the idea of being spanked. He was prepared to pay the large base sum Miranda requested and promised there'd be plenty of tips, too. It was way out in the boondocks of Virginia, in a county I'd never even been to. Tony and a friend of his picked us up that night. Julianne and I packed our best outfits and equipment into big bags. She was cool as ice and I kept asking her what we were supposed to DO. I mean, I thought we'd have planned a routine or something.

'This ain't Star Search, honey,' was all she said. 'Follow my lead, and we'll be fine.'

I had to just go with it. We pulled up to a big split-level in the woods. The sounds of music and men yelling and laughing floated outside. Tony walked us up the steps and a thirty-something guy answered the door with a beer in his hand. He introduced himself, and even shook hands with Tony and offered him a beer. He ushered us to a back bedroom without anyone else seeing. Coincidentally, some of Tony's friends were having a party about a

129

mile down the same road. Since we felt comfortable with the host and Julianne had pepper-spray in her bag, we gave him the go-ahead to leave and return in an hour and a half, when our show would be over. The host left us alone in the back bedroom and assured us of our privacy. Julianne gave him a tape of music to start in exactly ten minutes. He said he'd point out the bachelor once we got out there, then left us to change. In all my nervousness I'd forgotten my g-string to wear under the outfit. Julianne said not to worry, it wouldn't matter. She tried to get me to sip her beer to calm myself down, but I've always hated beer and couldn't force myself to do it. She hugged me once we were dressed and handed me a paddle that had one fluffy side and one hard leather side. 'Just carry this and follow me. You'll be great, I promise,' she said. She had more confidence in me than I did. I took a deep breath and hoped I wouldn't faint. The music started and I followed her out. A huge area in front of a fireplace was cleared, bordered by couches and chairs. There were about fifteen men, some sitting, some standing in a semi-circle around the open area we walked into. They had drinks in their hands and they all raised their bottles and cheered as we entered. 'Women!!! Wooo-hoo!' they yelled. The best man had his hand on the shoulder of a seated guy dressed in a crisp white shirt and khakis. His face was beet red

130

and plastered with a huge smile. Obviously, he was the groom. Julianne started cracking her whip and walking around the circle in her bad-ass way, staring each of the men in the eyes as she strutted by. They were mesmerized. I went counter-clockwise waving my paddle, which wasn't nearly as dramatic as a whip, but the hoots and whistles kept coming. With the music in the background I felt like we were going to strip, but we didn't. Julianne yelled, 'Okay, who's the lucky man?' Of course, all the groom's buddies pointed him out, and she went over and pulled him out of his chair.

'How old are you?' she asked, playfully.

'Th-th-thirty-three,' he answered.

'Bend over, boy. I'm here to give you a little going away present.' He did as she instructed while everyone clapped and whistled in approval. She sat on his back, facing his butt, and proceeded to whack away, saying things like 'You better be good to your wife, or else you'll get one of THESE . . . or one of THESE.'

'WoooHooo! Yeeeeehawwww!' the crowd cheered with every smack.

The groom smiled in ecstasy, thanking her after each one. Forgetting I was there to work, too, I just watched and cheered along until one of the guys came stumbling drunk up to me and said 'Can I get some, too?' I ordered him on his knees and before I knew it, I had a line of conservative-looking J.Crew-model-types waiting to be paddled! I smacked each one's behind several times while the others watched, then sent them on their way. Julianne kept the groom busy after his whipping by smothering his face with her huge chest. When the line ended and they were all rubbing their bottoms and laughing at what an unusual night it was turning out to be, the host came over and thanked us for our 'excellent performance.'

The men all offered us drinks and wanted to talk. Julianne downed a beer with them while I giggled and flirted and fielded all their slurred trying-to-be-polite-but-drunken questions. 'How old are you? How'd you start doing this? Are you a stripper, too? Do you have a business card?'

The host pulled us to the side and asked us for one final 'act.' He asked if we could do a golden shower. Not ON anyone, but just in front of everyone. He also asked if we could do some sort of lesbian act. Julianne was bisexual, but I wasn't and didn't want to do that, so she told him we'd 'come up with something.' We walked back to the back bedroom to change outfits and catch our breath. We were both hyper and amped on adrenaline. 'You'd think with all this beer I'd have to pee, but I don't,' Julianne said. 'Can you do it?'

My stage-fright was a fading memory as I answered with an enthusiastic 'yes!'

She said we should go out, dance around

with our props a little, then lay down like we're getting ready to do some masturbation or lesbian scene to get 'em all riled up, then she'd unsnap the crotch to my outfit, back up, and I'd let loose. I took a deep breath and agreed. I couldn't believe I was doing this, but I felt safe and comfortable and figured it was a once-in-a-lifetime thing.

While we were talking, one of the drunk guys wandered into the bedroom and offered Julianne fifty bucks for a blowjob, so she punched him in his gut and pushed him back into the hall. That gave me pause, but he was so drunk I'm sure he had no idea what just happened to him.

The music came on and we made our entrance once again to the front room, where the floor was now covered with a vinyl tarp. We waved our props and stomped dramatic-ally around the circle again, smiling and teasing the men. They yelled and reached out their hands trying to grab us and we swatted them, one by one, with our toys. It was all in good fun. Julianne laid down on the floor and was wiggling to the music. She grabbed my leg and acted like she was pulling me down next to her. I lay down, too. The men gathered in closer, wondering what was going to happen. They were cheering and throwing money onto the tarp. Julianne nodded, giving me the signal to end the night with the shower. I squatted near her, and she unsnapped my crotch and asked the crowd, 'should she do it?' The men went crazy. As they hollored and clapped I let loose a drizzle of pee. I couldn't believe I was doing this in front of a room full of people! The groom stood directly in front and just yelled 'Yeah! Yeah! Yeah!' over and over again, like he was at a football game, while some of his friends were shocked and standing with their mouths gaped open. I snapped my outfit back up, took a bow, and retreated to the bedroom.

Julianne came back a few minutes later with our tips, which I'd forgotten all about. It added up to about $150 and the host tipped us an extra $100 as well. We each walked away with around $400 that night. Julianne gave me extra since I did the golden. Unlike my stripping days, most of the men here were complete gentlemen. We had a great time and I'm sure they had a bachelor party they'd never forget.

Tony picked us up and brought us to his friends' party in a log-cabin-like house way back in the woods. We walked into a room full of longhaired guys drinking cheap beer and blasting Metallica. 'DOMINATRIXES! Awright!' they cheered as we walked in. Same reaction, completely different crowd. I was not very out about what I did for a living at the time, so I shot Tony a dirty look as if to ask, 'WHY did you tell them?' He smirked and winked at me, assuring me they were cool with it. It turned out they were. We stayed 'til four in the morning partying with them, and Julianne even picked up a young metalhead stud for herself.

A few months later, Julianne quit, saying she was 'lifestyle' now (she allowed slaves to live with her and wait on her hand and foot), and that we were all a bunch of fakes. I was getting the hang of things on my own, and trying to get creative. I had to – otherwise an hour could be difficult to fill. Smack smack smack and 'you bad bad boy' got real old, real quick.

I tied up one slave's balls and penis with a big red bow on my birthday, then strapped him to our bondage table and covered him with chocolate frosting, making him my human birthday cake. As a grand finale, I stuck a little pink candle in his pee-hole and lit it. He winced in pain, but later told me that it was the most exciting thing he'd ever done. Miranda took photos of the whole thing for his scrapbook, she said.

I got into public humiliation. I'd take certain slaves to the high-dollar Tyson's Corner mall, collars around their necks, while I dragged them from store to store making them buy me outfits and shoes from Macy's and Bloomie's. Verbal humiliation became my forté. For some reason insults just rolled off my tongue (blame it on growing up in a rough neighborhood). Sometimes I couldn't even believe the words coming from my mouth. I learned a lot from Miranda in this arena, too. 'You fat, sloppy sorry excuse-for-a-man,' I'd say. 'Get out of my sight. Why don't you go home to your over-priced hermetically-sealed house and jerk that little sausage you call a prick until it's raw while thinking about me and all the pussy you'll never get?' It was a great way to let off steam – harmless and fun. They never objected. They just kept coming back for more.

Some slaves wrote me detailed letters, with their fantasies excruciatingly spelled out. It helped me to get a feel for what they wanted, but I really didn't care to follow instructions. I'd give a shopping list to some, having them bring me small but costly items – specific shampoos, bubble bath, new handcuffs – whatever I needed. The lazy ones claimed to 'forget,' of course, expecting me to punish them more, but then I'd refuse to see them. They were just like little children – you couldn't give in and play their little games.

I found the most intense sessions involved sensory deprivation and more psychological aspects. When a client was blindfolded and tied up, he was utterly helpless and under my control. I liked this. I would make threats to leave them in their condition for longer than the agreed-upon hour, or fish a business card out of their wallets and say I was going to call their companies to explain why they'd be late.

I'd never really follow through with those things, but the mere thought sure made 'em squirm, and this entertained me.

If I wanted to truly scare them, I'd get out the scissors. Just a few snipping sounds near their genitals was enough to make most pour with sweat and fear. I actually did snip off a few locks of hair a couple of times, just for dramatic effect.

I really enjoyed the sexual control. I didn't aim for total control in this area with the married men – just the single ones. I'd order them to refrain from masturbating during the week and to 'save it all up' for their sessions with me. To my astonishment, they did! I loved the idea of having that much power over someone. Of course, if their sessions were few and far between, they'd break down and wouldn't be able to keep up their end of the bargain, but they always confessed this to me, along with the number of times they had failed and number of times their little fantasies involved me. I looked forward to doing that with a boyfriend someday.

I really had fun with the fetishes. I never knew so many existed! We got requests for big feet, small feet, smelly feet, feet in boots, feet in heels. Fur, plastic, leather and rubber were all common fetishistic fantasies. Tickling, smoking and even pie-throwing! (I'm serious!) Some men wanted to be diapered and treated as babies. These infuriated me the most for some reason – they brought out the 'abusive mom' in me. I stopped accepting this type after awhile because I just didn't need the annoyance. Some men had a fat fetish. Brianne, a 300-lb. dom-on-call, made more money than all of us just for letting these guys squish her fat between their fingers!

One regular wanted me to fart in his face. Not IN his face – ON his face, all while wearing old-fashioned panties, stockings and a mid-calf-length skirt (which he provided, with tags still on them). Once a week I'd walk up to his tiny third-floor room (I have no idea how he explained my visits to his roommates). There were yellow nicotine rings around the sad clown paintings that hung on his walls. The place reeked of cigarettes and alcohol, and he offered me some every week, looking at me quizzically each time I declined. I'd take the clothes from the hangers, go to the bathroom to change, then return to re-enact the scenario he painstakingly explained to me on my first night there. While he laid his tiny five-foot-four-inch frame on the floor (completely clothed) I was to pace back and forth, carefully stepping over his body and face, then reprimand him for 'trying to peek up my skirt.' After exactly twenty minutes (he timed it) we were to move to the bed, where he'd lie, with a pillow placed above his head for my knees. Then I'd sit facing the wall (away from him) and plant my butt right on his face – with his nose wedged right into my crack (through the material!) There he waited for me to fart as many times as possible until our hour was up. At first I thought this scenario was some kind of a joke, like 'let's see what I can get her to do?' but after a few weeks, I can honestly say this man thoroughly enjoyed it! I questioned him incessantly about what he was getting out of our meetings, but got no real answers. Maybe he didn't even know himself. He was an ex-Navy guy who scraped to pay for these weekly encounters (not to mention all the new underwear!) Sometimes he even called the agency twice a week, if he had a little extra spending money. I wasn't always able to 'perform,' (Taco Bell bean burrito or not, sometimes you just couldn't predict these things!) I became bored with his unwillingness to deviate from the script whatsoever, so I gave my Fart Man to Alisha as her first regular. Besides, she had chronic gas, so she could probably fulfill his needs better anyway. He certainly wasn't fulfilling mine.

In academia I was discovering Gloria Steinem, Naomi Wolf, Toni Morrison, Camille Paglia. I felt my job was a feminist endeavor. Sure, some would argue that I was still being viewed as a sex-object, but I had no objections to that. I liked it, in fact. I was equalizing the patriarchal power structure in my own way, for at least one hour each day. And the thing I liked about most fetishes was that they were not about beauty – not in the tradition way. It was all about whatever the object of obsession was. If a man loved black women, so be it – there was no way I could fulfill his fantasy. If a big man wanted to be whipped by a small woman, I fit the bill. I think everyone has their own fetish, whether they're aware of it or not. They may just be called 'preferences.' But if someone only dates Asian girls, or black men, or redheads, what do you think that is?

Foot fetishes were always my favorite. Looking back on it, all of my steady boyfriends have been foot-worshippers without even knowing the term! (Though I'd like to think it was just MY feet they worshipped!) I think I could have an orgasm with a good foot-rub and no other stimulation whatsoever. It feels so good when done correctly by a pair of strong, gentle hands. Sitting back in a chair with a man at my feet is the ultimate expression of power and pleasure for me. Sometimes I allowed small kisses on them, and scrubbing and pedicures were saved for only the most devoted regulars. (Most men can't paint a toenail worth shit!)

I swear a good massage and string of sincere compliments could make any woman become a most appreciative, feminine creature. I know from experience. One night, hanging at my house with two male friends, I had a fantasy of my own come true accidentally. Neither one knew I was a dominatrix, and I knew they didn't like each other but both liked me. I don't know how it all came about, but one of them asked if I wanted a back massage because he always felt that my shoulders were rock-hard. I said sure, and laid down, allowing him to pull up the back of my shirt and unsnap my bra. He commented to the other guy how stiff my muscles were. The other guy put his hands on, to check, and before I knew it, I was bathed in the luxury of four-handed massage! No sex or anything even close to it ever took place, but all that energy and attention made it an ecstatic evening I'll never forget. Highly recommended.

Keep thy heart with all diligence, for out of it are the issue of life.
– Bad Brains (Proverbs: 4)

I learned my limits. One time a young African American man came in and before his session he told me he wanted to be called 'nigger' and other names degrading his background and skin color. I took his money and agreed. After instructing him to his knees, I left to go change, all the while asking myself if I could do such a horrible thing.

I couldn't.

It scraped my soul raw just thinking about it. I gave the call to Miranda and she had no problem insulting him just as he wished. Because of the pain I'd gone through in defending my old relationship, I just didn't have those feelings in my heart. I don't know why it just wasn't in me, but it wasn't. It was something that went so against my own moral grain that I couldn't even pretend through it. It also made me realize that maybe I wasn't really 'acting' in my other sessions, as I thought I had been.

Demographically, most of our clients were wealthy older Caucasian men, so fortunately I didn't lose a lot of business because of my little 'problem.'

Another time an old man wanted me to stand over him and spit in his face and insult him repeatedly. In theory it sounded fine. But when I started, and he flinched with loogie after loogie, I gave up. 'That was only ten minutes! We have another fifty minutes together,' he whined. 'Our session's over. Get out,' I said and turned my back to him. The door shut and a tear ran down my face. I wondered what I was doing. Was I really evil, or was I a failed dominatrix? When I explained it to Miranda she said he got exactly what he wanted anyway. Me throwing him out was the ultimate rejection. The thought comforted me a little.

My only enema experience happened by accident. Miranda paged me while I was studying at the school library one afternoon.

I found a pay phone and called her back.

'Alexis, you wear a size seven, right?' she asked.

'Umm . . . depends on what I'm wearing.'

'This guy has a nurse fantasy, and he already has the uniform – size seven. I've seen him before, so don't worry about it. He's easy.' I scrambled for pen and took down directions to his Bethesda home. When I got there a half hour later, a forty-ish gentleman with sandy brown newscaster-like hair parted on the side greeted me at the door.

'You're perfect,' he said as he ushered me in. His house was pretty plush. Overstuffed sofas, a fireplace, chandeliers. He walked up some stairs, and I followed him all the way to the master bedroom, where he was taking a white nursing uniform off of a hanger.

'Size seven?'

'Yeah,' I said. He handed it to me and pointed to the hall bathroom.

'You can change in there. I'll be waiting in here for you.'

In the bathroom I stripped and squeezed into the uniform, thinking, *Size seven my ass!* It was the smallest size seven I'd ever seen, and I couldn't even button it all the way over my small 36Bs. I pinned my hair up and walked back out to the bedroom.

He was lying on the bed with his pants off (shirt still on) facing the wall, away from me.

'Go ahead. The enema bottles are on the

dresser,' he said, not even looking back at me.

I didn't know the fantasy would involve an enema. I thought I'd just pretend to give him an exam or something. Euuuu. I saw twelve little plastic bottles on the dresser and figured I had my work cut out for me.

'That's twelve enemas! I'll be here all night! You only paid $200, for one,' I said angrily.

'No, that counts as one. Altogether it only adds up to sixteen ounces, the normal amount for one enema.'

'Then why did you get twelve small ones?'

'Because it takes longer. I like it better that way.'

Ugh. Just what I was afraid of. I wasn't gonna stand around and argue enema particulars with him, so I put on a pair of my disposable surgeon gloves and picked up the first bottle. I'd never done one before, but it wasn't rocket science. I put some lubricant on the top and inserted it into his anus with a disgusted look on my face, I'm sure. I thought everything was going fine until he started to whine.

'Can you put your hand on my butt?' he asked.

'What?'

'Just one hand holding my butt cheek, while the water's going in?'

'No, I won't do that. Now be quiet and take your enema,' I said, in dominatrix-mode.

'Please?' I could tell he was frustrated, but I just wasn't going to give in.

144

'I said no. Now be quiet.'

So much for my bedside manner. I'll spare you the details of the remaining eleven bottles being emptied into my problem patient, but I told Miranda I never wanted to do a nurse fantasy again.

'Have you gained weight?'

'No.'

'Lost?'

'No!'

'Colored your hair?'

'No, why?!'

'What are you wearing? Pink is a submissive color. Take that off!'

These were typical greetings at Miranda's. She was always attentive to our looks, how we were dressing, how we presented ourselves. Looking back, I understand that it was just her way of protecting her investments. But at times I felt like a slave on the auction block. Never before had I worried so much about my hair, my make-up, my clothes – things that were so trivial in my life before. Punk rock sensibilities had kept me from fretting over the societal acceptability of my exterior. But now I had to think about it more than I liked. I had to be sure I looked like a dominatrix, at least in-session. The other girls always did that 'once-over' look-you-up-and-down-thing to me, smirking with distaste at the sweatshirts and cut-offs I usually wore. They even called my Doc Martens 'men's hiking boots.' Miranda told them to shut up, that as long as I looked beautiful in-session and no clients complained, I was fine.

I wore her outfits until I got regulars to take me to the Pleasure Chest, an expensive fetish shop in Georgetown, to buy me my own. I had two patent-leather teddies and one plastic-like skirt made out of PVC (the same stuff my dad used to fix pipes, from what I remembered.) My hair looked great at the beginning of each session but always found its natural curl and frizz by the end of the hour. With Miranda's help I perfected my lipstick before sessions, only to smear the awful-tasting stuff off afterwards while heading home, trying to feel normal again. I felt beautiful with my clients, but amateur and unfeminine next to the other doms. In the typical dom gear they looked comfortable, like true girly-girls (I was sure they had looked just as comfortable in their high school cheerleading outfits), while I felt like a caricature of a dominatrix – a tomboy in drag. I felt silly looking at myself in the mirror sometimes.

One day while in session, it all just got to me. I was uncomfortable, dammit! My toes were pinched in narrow stilettos, my waist cinched by a corset – I thought, wait a minute, HE's the one who's supposed to be in bondage.

'Remove my shoes, you stupid slut,' I ordered.

Of course, he did . . . and with that, I was free. From then on I was the barefoot dominatrix. I'm sure high heels were designed by some man, anyway.

Ass-play, as they called it in the biz, in general made me queasy, to be quite honest. The enema thing made me gag, and when Miranda shoved ice-cubes up a slave's rectum, I was astounded at her creativity and his body's capabilities (he took 21 cubes!) but had no desire to try it myself. They started melting and he had to run to the bathroom, which was way too messy for me. I watched her do dildo-training on a few clients before trying it on my own at the beginning of Junior year. I was curious about the power – how DOES it feel to fuck someone, rather than be fucked? I used to needle old boyfriends with these kind of questions, which they never fully answered.

My first try was with a wrestling client. I should've known right then it wouldn't work out – I hated the thought of wrestling a client – all that physical contact – so I had never accepted that fetish before. Miranda, sales-woman that she was, talked me into it, saying she was short on girls and he was easy and she'd done him a million times.

'All he wants is for you to pin him down, tie him up, and do a little dildo training,' she said.

I was uncomfortable with the thought, but

took a deep breath and said, 'I can do this.' I
changed into wrestling gear (a black spandex
number) and entered the room.

'How old are you?' the slave asked.

'Shut the fuck up,' I answered. 'I'll ask the
questions here.'

'What are you, like twelve?'

He pushed the wrong buttons and un-
fortunately, I reacted. I jumped on him and
struggled to get him onto the floor. The touch
of his sweaty slippery skin disgusted me. After
a few minutes of this, I finally got him onto his
stomach and started to tie his hands together
behind him. I couldn't believe I was actually
breaking a sweat! It pissed me off even more.
He bucked and flipped over before I could get
the ropes tied. I kneed him in the chest, which
shut him down for a good minute – enough
time to tie him up. Breathing hard, I got out
the largest dildo from Miranda's collection. I
covered it with a condom, as she required us
to do, and talked tough while I began to
penetrate him.

'You wanna play rough? I'll show you rough,
ass-boy. How's that feel?'

I slid the rubber dick into his small asshole
and felt a slight resistance. I pushed harder
while he whined. Before I knew what was
happening, the dildo popped back out, falling
onto the floor, and I couldn't help but notice
the condom covered in shit.

'You disgusting pig!' I shrieked. I honestly

didn't know what to do. I was so grossed out by the sight and smell of his waste, I began to panic.

'You stay right there, filthy whore.' Miranda's words were coming out of my mouth. I left the room and ran to the waiting room for help.

'It's gross! Help!' I said to Miranda and the other girl sitting there.

'Whaddya mean? Go in there and finish him off,' she laughed.

'I can't. I didn't want to do this, and then you talked me into it, and now there's shit everywhere, and I'm about to throw up—'

I ran to the bathroom with my hand over my mouth.

Miranda went back into the room with the slave and finished the session. I waited in the back room until he left – I was embarrassed.

'He actually liked you,' she said afterward, watching as I changed back into my regular clothes.

'Prick. Why – what'd he say?'

'He said you were strong. You just couldn't tie a knot or use a dildo for shit.'

'Well, he's a disgusting pig and—'

'He wants to see you again next week.'

'Huh? Well, I don't care. I will never see him again and I will never be talked into a session I don't wanna to do again.'

'When that happens with a dildo, all you do

is yell at them and tell 'em to do an enema before they come next time. It's no big deal. I do it all the time.' She had an answer for everything, I swear.

'I don't care. I'm never doing that again. It disgusts me and I just don't want to do it. I'm the dominatrix and I can do whatever I want, remember?'

I felt like Frankenstein's monster. She didn't like having her words thrown back in her face.

I packed my bags quietly and said, 'See ya' with tears in my eyes. I could not be her. Maybe I couldn't do this kind of work anymore.

GRADUATION

I went solo. First I called Alisha at Miranda's, to see if she wanted to start a business with me or work for me, but she refused to talk to me. I guess I wasn't in the clique anymore. I decided not to play their seventh-grade do-you-like-me-circle-one-yes-no bullshit games, but to live by my own rules this time – do what was comfortable for me. I placed my own ads in the paper and booked my own calls, just outcalls, since I couldn't afford a separate incall apartment and certainly didn't want slaves coming to my place. I still did foot fetishes, spankings, whipping, golden showers and everything I liked, only now I kept all of the money from each session. I tried to get Tricia into it with me again, but she was still reluctant.

It was junior year and I declared communications as my major since I'd already taken a lot of the required courses and it seemed as good as any other. With the exception of math, I excelled in most of my classes. My teachers loved my enthusiasm and offbeat paper and the project-topics on things like body-piercing, hip-hop music as an art-form, Latin murals, D.C. parks – whatever piqued my interest at the time. For the first time in my life I felt rewarded for my individuality. Financially I was on stable ground for once, but I was creatively frustrated, too. I still wasn't sure what I wanted to do when I was done with school, but knew it had be something more fulfilling. I thought I was turning into a pretty good communicator as a dominatrix and figured I could apply those skills somewhere else. Too bad it didn't count as an internship.

I was much happier working independently. I felt more like myself. My sessions were more natural. I'd ask my unsuspecting clients personal questions, and share whatever new tidbits were on my mind each evening, making it relevant to their own 'lessons.' My eyes sucked words from textbook pages as fast as I could turn them during my studies, and my mouth was more than happy to spit all I learned back out.

The Elizabethan period was most interesting. 'The good servant is attentive. The best servant is a little bit psychic,' I'd read to an aspiring submissive. 'The worst kind whines during session and breaks his promises constantly!' I'd improvise.

I did everything I could to reform any man's

bad behavior. Punished them. Lectured them. Forced them to buy flowers and presents for their wives and girlfriends. Even encouraged them to talk more to their wives and girlfriends. The lack-of-communication they spoke of scared me off from marriage more than ever. I never wanted that. When I stopped being concerned about their personal lives, I'd just lure them in, listen to their stories, take their money, then BAM, holy threshold, Batman – out came Evil Alexis, ready to play 'cruel child with helpless pet' or 'let's do a lab experiment' or, my favorite, 'queen of the world.'

I wasn't as stone-faced as I used to be during sessions. I laughed or giggled outright whenever the urge hit me. I even smiled throughout my torturous actions. I was still my own sweet self at the end of it all, and I had new stories for Tricia every night.

Relations with my family were still lapsed, except for my sister, who worked at a bank and seemed intrigued by the stories I told her over hours of long-distance phone calls. At least I wasn't asking them or anyone else for money, and that was a freedom I needed.

As for my social life, I did meet one man who seemed up to the challenge of having a relationship with me – Michael, an Irish electrician from New York a friend had set me up with. Excellent sense of humor. Made good money. I liked that he worked with his hands, like my dad. He believed in my 'good brain,' as he put it, more than anyone ever had. He even offered to pay for the rest of my college education – once we got married. Believe me, I entertained the thought. I was making good money, but not enough to afford all of my private college's tuition. It would've been nice to have someone take care of me in a way I had never experienced before, but I couldn't do it with a clear conscience. I cared for him, but I knew I wasn't in love with him. And I knew I had to pay for school myself, no two ways about it. Plus I was scared to death of marriage.

Whenever I did get a little lonely, I looked back into my old journals. 'Day dream about the beautiful boy with a broad brown back.' I must've been in ninth grade when I wrote that. It wasn't about anybody in particular, just a vague idea of my dream man. When Tricia and I commiserated over man problems, I always said 'I just want someone to love, respect and worship me. Is that so much to ask?' She always laughed, but I was dead serious.

I had faith he was out there somewhere, and knew he might not even be in D.C. at all. He could be traveling the world, for all I knew. I didn't care how much money he made or where he came from. I wanted him to be my peer. I knew my clients would jump at the chance to 'serve' me the rest of my life, but most of them seemed too old and wimpy. Plus I wanted someone who thought I was sexy in a T-shirt and jeans, not just dom-wear or the girly uniform the world expected. Someone who would love me in my sweatpants and no make-up. Through my job I was learning that sex was more than just a sweaty night in bed. It could be so many things . . . it could be an adventure, with a loving and willing partner. That's how I wanted it to be. Sure, I had physical desires, but I continued to see boys as unnecessary distractions for the time being. I still felt there would be plenty around later. I had good friends, and I just wanted to finish college and make myself into something to be proud of first.

One night I got a request for a brown shower. I thought about how I'd never done one at Miranda's, and figured what the hell? One woman's feces was another man's fetish, right? I called up Julianne for advice. I was surprised – she was happy to hear from me. She said she'd been excluded from Miranda's little clique since leaving, too. We commiserated, reminisced about the funny bachelor party we did together, then agreed we would work independently but support one another in the name of sisterhood. Julianne instructed me on how to handle a brown. She said to eat nothing but beans and veggies the day before, which is what I usually ate anyway. She said to take a laxative that night before, and have the appointment with the guy for first thing in the morning. I followed her instructions to the tee. When the gentleman (a doctor) arrived at eight a.m. I was a little nervous but tried not to let it show. He stripped and lay eagerly in the bathtub while my lower abdomen rumbled. I knew the time was near. I unsnapped the crotch of my outfit and hung my white ass over the edge of the tub, facing the sink and toilet, away from him, just as Julianne said. I heard him scoot over. I told him not to make any noise and yelled at him not to touch me, that he was my toilet slut and nothing more. Sharp pains poked my stomach, my body got hot and sweaty, and then I let loose. My only mistake was in looking back. I saw my excrement on his face and the pig was licking his lips, eating it! I threw up all over him, then turned around and wiped my face with a towel, embarrassed. 'No extra charge,' I said. I remembered Miranda talking about a rare Roman shower fetish, where people liked you to throw up on them. Ugh – who knew WHY, but they did. This man didn't seem to mind, but I ordered him to take a shower and leave, never to return. He called begging for another session a week later. I asked him straight up, 'You're a doctor, right? So tell me, is it safe to eat some-one else's shit?' He stammered and hemmed and hawed, then finally told me that urine is sterile, but fecal matter is not. I don't know why he wanted to do what he did, but I decided I didn't have to be any part of it. I wasn't even interested in his reasons. It was as disgusting as I expected and I never did it again. I told him off, and he finally stopped calling.

Even though I got to do pretty much whatever I wanted to these men, I was quite sick of fulfilling fantasies. College was ending and I wanted to fulfill myself. For someone working in the infamous sex industry, I was really quite a prude. I started using these men in ways they could better help me. When I had tax problems, an accountant slave could be counted on to help me out. Parking tickets were magically erased by law enforcement. Doctors gave me and my hypochondriac friends free advice and checkups. Lawyers came in handy, too. I was getting bored with everything. I wanted to do something more, something different. As usual, that something happened by accident. One day at school I saw a flyer advertising a meeting for writers interested in the school's weekly newspaper. I went to the meeting and listened to the different department's editors (all male) describe their editorial needs. When the entertainment editor said he needed music story ideas, my hand shot up. I suggested a piece on an up-and-coming local band I knew. He shot it down, saying someone else was working on it already. I asked about another local band. And he said they weren't popular enough. A guy in the group raised his hand with an idea that made all the editors nod in lukewarm approval. Another girl raised her hand with a suggestion for covering a local play, and it was nixed right away, no explanations whatsoever. It became clear these boys just didn't want to play with the girls and didn't want any female hands in their newspaper. I thought back to an ad I'd seen in the paper recently, for a Public Enemy and Anthrax tour. Two big bands coming to play in a huge arena downtown. I raised my hand and blurted 'I'd like to interview either Anthrax or Public Enemy while they're here in town.' The entertainment editor's red eyebrows raised.

'Do you think it's possible?' he asked, not offering an ounce of help or encouragement. 'Of course, no problem,' I said, like I had some secret way in with the bands.

'If you can get an interview, we'll use it,' he said.

That was all I needed. 'I will,' I said confidently, and left the meeting hoping I'd never see him on campus again if I couldn't pull it off. I went home and dialed New York City information and got the numbers for Anthrax's record label, then PE's record label. Anthrax's said no right away, but Public Enemy's publicist gave me the name of a local rep I could contact to set up an interview with the band. I was skeptical, but when the time came, I got a damn good interview and published my first of many articles in the school paper. Like it or not, they had a female journalist on staff and I had my first taste of success, and it had nothing to do with my body or the way I looked. It was delicious, and I wanted more.

By the end of the year, Miranda called and said she missed me. She said I was like a little sister and wanted me to work for her again. To be honest, the way I made my living had started to get to me. I was sick of seeing penises all day. The job was more of an annoyance than fun anymore. Plus running a small business while going to school full time and writing and trying to have a social life made life more hectic than I wanted it to be. Miranda and I talked and struck a compromise. She asked me if I'd prefer just answering phones, which would free her up to have more of a life of her own. I liked the thought of working as little as possible through my last year of school – and writing for the school paper as a pleasant distraction. She told me I was the only girl she could ever trust with her home and her lines – she knew I didn't steal or lie, and I knew the ropes of the business well enough to know how to handle the phones. It worked out perfectly. I worked short, scheduled shifts and made either ten percent of each call I booked or ten dollars an hour, whichever was more at the end of the day. It kept my bills paid and my commitment to the business minimal. Plus I had my old friend back.

The phone job wasn't as easy as I expected – sometimes you'd get heavy breathers, you had to be careful of what you said about dildo training and such – but it didn't require me to dress up and look 'presentable' all the time or to carry a separate 'bag of tricks.' Since I'd been on the other end of things, I took extra care to make sure I got directions and room numbers right for the girls. I was prompt with the safety checks and good at determining the serious callers from the bozos. Some guys called wanting to get their kicks just by talking, but Miranda showed me how to handle them and not let them get a session for free, as she called it. I never admitted to them that I was a dom, and if they asked what I looked like Miranda said to say 'I'm 400 pounds with curlers in my hair, smoking and watching soap operas. Now do you want to book an appointment or not?' It usually turned them off or at the very least lightened things up and made them laugh.

Someone from *Playgirl* magazine called the business to interview me once. Miranda was against doing interviews, she told me, because 'they always wanna make you sound like a hooker.' But a writer friend of mine referred this woman to me because she wanted to talk to a dominatrix, so I agreed. How cool that I was the expert she was going to quote for her story! It'd all be anonymous, of course. She only knew my first name, and she'd use a fake one in the story, my friend said. I thought it'd be fun. That's how I get myself into most things.

The phone rang at the appointed time, and the reporter introduced herself in a friendly New Yawka-kinda tone. She asked me what a dominatrix was and what my average call was like. I gave her the basic rundown and client profile. Then she told me the article was actually on shame.

'Are you ashamed of what you do for a living?'

'No,' I answered.

'Do your friends know what you do?'

'Yeah, most of them.'

'Do your parents know what you're doing?' she asked.

'Um, no, but they—'

'Were you spanked as a child?'

'Occasionally.'

'A lot?' she asked.

'Just sometimes. What's a lot?'

'Did your parents abuse you as a child, I mean?' she continued. 'Do you think that's why you abuse people for money?'

'I wasn't abused. I abuse people for money because it's easy. I'm actually a writer,' I said.

'Yeah, I bet you could write some funny stuff

from your experiences, huh? Anyway, do you feel you were shamed as a child?' she asked.

'No.'

'Hmmm . . . well I'm not sure if this is gonna make it into the article,' she said disapprovingly. 'Either you're not telling me the truth, or you have no shame I can work with.'

I didn't know what to say.

'Umm . . . sorry.'

'Okay. Thanks for your time, honey. I'll call you when the article comes out.'

I shrugged at the phone as I put it down. I felt I'd disappointed her somehow. Not enough shame. Oh well. Why should I have any?

In my off time I was covering ground on the last bit of school that lay ahead of me. It was my last semester, and I had no idea what I wanted to do for the impending rest of my life. I used my hangout time at the club to meet bands and get more photographs than ever for the school paper, proud of each little byline I produced. I gathered my clips and eventually got published in some local papers, then finally a national magazine, which paid me all of thirty five dollars for my story. It was nothing compared to what I made with my other 'skills,' but it was enough to encourage me to do more. People in my family didn't become writers, so I never pictured that as a career option for after college, but I knew I'd found a way to combine my love for music and

162

writing. I had a creative outlet. The magazine I sold the story to was on the west coast, a place I'd never been, but had done my share of California dreamin' about through the harsh East coast winters. I kept in touch with them and wrote for them some more.

That summer was my last stretch of school. I needed an internship, and got a legitimate one as an assistant in a graphics department. It was full time during the day, unpaid, but it counted as a class. I still worked for Miranda in the evenings, and even took on a second internship for fun – one that didn't count for anything but my own satisfaction – as a marketing assistant, helping with publicity for bands that were traveling through. The office day-job was a little weird because I was bored most of the time. It was hard for me to sit still at a computer all day, and I wondered if I was a bit hyperactive. Plus I had to buy new clothes – shorts and T-shirts didn't cut it, and neither did black vinyl and platforms. I had no more classes to take, but between the office job, band stuff, writing for the paper, and working the phones, I was busier than ever, and it felt good. It was all for me, not some man paying me to act something out for him.

On the second of August, two days before my birthday, I turned in the required term paper about my internship experiences – my last paper – then drove home with tears and sweat covering my face. I couldn't believe I'd really done it. I made it through college. The first one in my family ever. I worked my ass off for this and it was finally over. So anti-climactic. So now what? I slept hard that night. My fan fought the humidity while I dreamed of ocean breezes.

GOODBYE

It was four months before the new year. I decided to start the next one in a new place, doing new things. I knew no one and had no steady job prospects there, but I felt the call of the west. I decided that on the first of January I'd be driving cross-country to the land of sunshine and the unknown.

I worked Miranda's phones and as a dom for the rest of the year, saving every penny I earned for my new life. The time I used to spend on classes I spent taking more calls. I admit my sessions became more impersonal and my clients were a nameless, faceless blur these months, but it didn't matter. I used them as stepping stones to get where I wanted, which is exactly what they should've wanted for me, too – to be happy, ultimately right? I also kept writing. Interviewing and reviewing bands. Keeping journals. Everyone had a story and I wanted to hear them all. I kicked my own ass to stay motivated, and vowed not to let easy money make me lazy. It was fun while it lasted, but now I wanted to be more than someone's fantasy. To my surprise and delight, I published again and again.

Come December, Miranda threw me a huge going-away party. She invited all the friends who knew about 'my secret life,' and all of the doms and favorite regulars. Instead of gifts, she set up a cash box for donations toward my new life. Most doms live passionately – and their generosity is no exception. Even women I was never friends with donated. I was over-whelmed by the amount of goodwill I received. The night's end brought tears to my eyes, then laughter as Miranda entered the room holding a brand new shiny red patent leather outfit with matching shoes and paddle. 'I know you're leaving the business, going "legit" and all, but you'll have this just in case,' she said. Later on Tony made us all almost pee our pants laughing when he came out wearing my outfit. There's nothing more beautiful than a tough guy unafraid of being goofy or looking soft. We all hugged and kissed our goodbyes, and at the end of the night Miranda slipped me an envelope which read DO NOT OPEN UNTIL YOU REACH THE WEST COAST in her curly handwriting. Tony gave me a silver ring he always wore, and a string of wooden beads for good luck, but left the party quietly, without even saying good-bye. It was no surprise – he told me ahead of time he would probably do that, because goodbye was just too painful and final to say.

I packed up my U-Haul in the morning, and left for my new adventure. While most of my classmates were walking down the aisle to get their diplomas, I was already in New Mexico, more than halfway to my destination. I was sad leaving my city and my friends. I knew I'd have to start from scratch in California. I'd probably join the workforce as an entry-level schmuck, like most other college grads. I knew how to make an extra buck if I ever needed to again, but I wanted to get away from that. Living a double life is extremely tiresome, and working as a dom got to be too draining – like having fifty boyfriends at once. I wanted just one eventually. And I wanted to use my mind to make it in the world. Domination was a means to an end, it wasn't my dream. Like a psychologist (I charged about the same!), I merely provided a much-needed service for my clients. Some of them really needed punishment for things I'll never fully know about, some just used me for entertainment – it was a two-way street I enjoyed dancing down. It wasn't horrible. It's just something that happened to me on the way to womanhood. Ironic that I was the disciplinarian, because I learned so much from this business and these men. Like that everyone gets their kicks in different ways – as long as no one's being held against their will (my clients came to ME, after all), there's nothing wrong with desire. Whether porno movies, strip clubs or S&M games, none's better than another. I'm no longer a scared girl struggling for anything. Now I know the power of being a woman, and it has nothing to do with what Madison Avenue wants us to believe – a dress size, a hair color, or fragrance. It has to do with the essence of femininity. As Maya Angelou wrote, 'phenomenal woman, that's me.' I'm lucky, because I got to experience what I've always felt every woman deserves – love, adoration, worship, confidence, respect. I could have stayed where I reigned queen of my scene, where I had a job that paid more than most, and where I had plenty of friends to keep me from boredom and loneliness, but that would've been the easy way, and I've never taken that route. It was time to push away from the safety of my wall.

That envelope contained a card from Miranda, bearing sweet words of friendship, which I'll treasure forever. Oh, and a big fat check, which came in handy as a security deposit on my apartment. I doubt college helped me very much with my career goals, but the job I did to get through gave me the skills I need to deal with the assholes we all encounter in life. The scene life is a memory now, but my dominant tendencies still reign. However I turn out, rich or poor, I honestly don't care. I'll be fine. I've got my self-respect. I've got the best friends in the world. I can take care of myself. That's what it's all about. I wield my will like a whip, and the world serves me well. Life is a kingdom I walk through proudly, knowing that I am the Queen of my destiny. I only wish the same for everyone else.

Miranda is still in the business. She says she hates it and will get out as soon as she has enough money to leave. Tony's pager number, his ever-changing lifeline, has been disconnected, and I heard he's doing some underground stuff in Miami, of all places. I miss him terribly and wonder if I'll ever see him again. Julianne still works on her own and heads a regional S&M support group. Tricia's in grad school, studying to be a social worker (and still tying her boyfriends up.) And I'm just another writer on the West coast. That red outfit's still in the back of my closet, 'just in case.'

But doms are a dime a dozen out here, so it wouldn't even be that profitable for me to come out of retirement. I don't want to anyway. I got what I wanted, and so did my clients. That's it. Now I know how to swim. Time for some new strokes.

THE GOOD GIRL'S GUIDE TO BAD GIRL SEX
An Indispensable Guide to Pleasure and
Seduction by Barbara Keesling Ph.D.

Imagine a world where you were as sexually
confident, physically uninhibited and intensely
orgasmic as you have always wanted to be. . .

Now, acclaimed sex therapist Dr Barbara
Keesling tells you how. Based on the understanding that inside every good girl is a bad girl
struggling to get out, *The Good Girl's Guide to*
Bad Girl Sex teaches women how to express their
natural impulses with dignity and panache. Bad
girls know no shame. Bad girls are comfortable
in their bodies. Bad girls always feel georgeous
and desirable!

Learn how to optimize your sexual power with
this frank, funny and thoroughly comprehensive
book. Packed with practical exercises, *The Good*
Girl's Guide includes insider information on the
sex toys you never knew you had, how to seduce
a man by simply walking into a room, how to
enjoy your G-spot and how to give (and receive!)
mind-blowing orgasms.

The Good Girl's Guide is the key to your sexual
future – an invaluable resource for the modern
woman.

A Bantam Paperback
0 553 81475 3

302 ADVANCED TECHNIQUES FOR DRIVING A MAN WILD IN BED
by Olivia St. Claire

The author of the hugely successful and perennially popular *203 Ways to Drive a Man Wild in Bed* is back with an all-new, easy-to-use guide that elevates sexual proficiency and erotic ecstasy to an entirely new level.

'The secret lies not in comeliness or technique but in the fearlessness to reveal your truest female self', writes Olivia St. Claire as she refines the art of driving him wild. Olivia helps you identify your passion triggers, safely guides you to the edge of your boundaries, and tells you everything you ever wanted to know about truly passionate lovemaking.

Frankly erotic, playfully sexy and intelligently written, *302 Advanced Techniques for Driving a Man Wild in Bed* is simple enough to consult at a moment's notice, but sophisticated enough to leave him breathless at your new-found prowess. The inviting layout and the numbered tips make it easy and fun for a willing couple to embark upon an amorous adventure – whenever and wherever the spirit moves them. Users of this dazzling selection of sexual techniques will bring any man to his knees.

A Bantam Paperback
0 553 81473 7

MOUTH MUSIC made easy
How to drive her wild with pleasure
by Harry and Caddie Youngberry

You've sent her flowers, written her love poems, told her she's the woman of your dreams. But now you want to dazzle her; take her beyond her every desire and into the realms of ecstasy. . .

This humorous and practical book tells you how to drive women wild – with your tongue. This candid guide to oral sex will give you the confidence to develop your natural talents and teach you how to become a red-hot lover.

0 552 14973 X

HOT SEX: HOW TO DO IT
POCKET EDITION
by Tracey Cox

'Frank, forthright and at times hysterically funny'
Cosmopolitan

Now you can have fantastic sex wherever you go with the *Hot Sex* pocket edition. It serves up all the juiciest bits in a handy take-anywhere size. It's practical, explicit and fun, with hundreds of steamy tips which will have you shredding the sheets and begging for more:

• The famous 10-step guide to gving him a hellishly good blow-job.
• Ohmigod-don't-ever-stop oral sex for her
• The hot new way to have intercourse (guaranteed to up her orgasm quota)
• His and her how-to-find-it guides to your G-spots
• Sex toys tried and tested
• Enough foreplay ideas to keep you amused for days, weeks, months. . .

Tracey Cox is one of the world's foremost (and hottest) writers on sex and relationships and is also a TV presenter. Her numerous appearances include *Hotter Sex*, *Would Like to Meet* as well as regular slots on the *Lorraine* show.

0 552 14956 X

HOT LOVE: HOW TO GET IT
POCKET EDITION
by Tracey Cox

'Do not even attempt to fall in love or stay in love without this book'
Cosmopolitan

The must-have mini-manual for everyone. *HOT LOVE* shows you how to have a great relationship – and how to keep it that way. This pocket edition of the bestselling original, *Hot Relationships*, has all the answers to your dating and relating dilemmas. Packed with advice on everything from flirting to flings, monogamy and marriage including:

• The Meet Market – where to find the love of your life
• Why Love is a Drug and the six stages of intoxication
• How and when to say 'I love you'
• 'Playing house'
• Why sex is the glue which will stick you together
• The eight most frequently-asked couple sex questions

Tracey Cox is one of the world's foremost (and hottest) writers on sex and relationships, and is also a TV presenter. Her numerous appearances include *Would Like to Meet* and *Hotter Sex*, along with a regular slot on the *Lorraine* show.

0 552 14955 1

STORY OF O
by Pauline Reage

One of the most famous erotic novels of all time.

'A rare thing, a pornographic book well written and without a trace of obscenity'
Graham Greene

'A highly literary and imaginative work, the brilliance of whose style leaves no one in doubt whatever of the author's genius . . . a profoundly disturbing book, as well as a black tour-de-force'
Spectator

'Here all kinds of terrors await us, but like a baby taking its mother's milk all pains are assuaged. Touched by the magic of love, everything is transformed. *Story of O* is a deeply moral homily'
J.G. Ballard

'Cool, cruel, formalistic fantasy about a woman subjected – at the price of the greatest love of her life – to the gamut of male sado-masochistic urges'
Birmingham Post

0 552 08930 3

A SELECTED LIST OF NON-FICTION TITLES AVAILABLE FROM CORGI AND BANTAM BOOKS

81440 0	THE ART OF EFFORTLESS LIVING	Ingrid Bacci	£7.99
09806 X	WHAT DO YOU SAY AFTER YOU SAY HELLO?	Eric Berne M.D.	£5.99
81354 4	THE BOOK OF ANSWERS	Carol Bolt	£9.99
81487 7	THE BOOK OF LOVE ANSWERS	Carol Bolt	£9.99
14707 9	HOT SEX	Tracey Cox	£7.99
14784 2	HOT RELATIONSHIPS	Tracey Cox	£7.99
14956 X	HOT SEX POCKET EDITION	Tracey Cox	£4.99
14955 1	HOT LOVE POCKET EDITION	Tracey Cox	£4.99
14938 1	THE FABULOUS GIRL'S GUIDE TO DECORUM	Kim Izzo & Ceri Marsh	£6.99
81496 6	ZEN AND THE ART OF FALLING IN LOVE	Charlotte Kasl	£6.99
81475 3	THE GOOD GIRL'S GUIDE TO BAD GIRL SEX	Barbara Keesling	£6.99
81326 9	THE PURSUIT OF HAPPINESS	Robert Kelsey	£6.99
08930 3	STORY OF O	Pauline Reage	£6.99
12571 7	STORY OF O PART II	Pauline Reage	£5.99
81371 4	LIFE MAKEOVERS	Cheryl Richardson	£7.99
50473 8	203 WAYS TO DRIVE A MAN WILD IN BED	Olivia St Claire	£5.99
50485 1	227 WAYS TO UNLEASH THE SEX GODDESS IN EVERY WOMAN	Olivia St Claire	£5.99
81473 7	302 ADVANCED TECHNIQUES FOR DRIVING A MAN WILD IN BED	Olivia St Claire	£6.99
81415 X	THE MAGICAL GARDEN	Sophia with Denny Sargent	£7.99
81488 5	THE ORACLE BOOK	Georgia Routsis Savas	£9.99
40397 4	THE FRAGRANT PHARMACY	Valerie Ann Worwood	£9.99
50579 3	THE FRAGRANT HEAVENS	Valerie Ann Worwood	£8.99
40799 6	THE FRAGRANT MIND	Valerie Ann Worwood	£9.99
14973 X	MOUTH MUSIC MADE EASY	Harry and Caddie Youngberry	£3.99